DISCOVERING
ANIMALS

Also by Tony Soper

The bird table book
The Shell book of beachcombing
Penguins (with John Sparks)
Owls (with John Sparks)
Wildlife begins at home
Everyday birds
Beside the sea (with Hilary Soper)
Birdwatch
Discovering birds
The National Trust book of the coast

DISCOVERING ANIMALS

An introduction to
British land and freshwater mammals

Tony Soper

Illustrated by John Busby

BRITISH BROADCASTING CORPORATION

This book accompanies the BBC Continuing Education Television series *Discovering Animals*, first broadcast on BBC2 from Autumn 1985.

Series introduced by Tony Soper and produced by Bryn Brooks.

Published to accompany a series of programmes prepared in consultation with the BBC Continuing Education Advisory Council.

This book is set in 10½ on 12 point Ehrhardt. Phototypeset on Linotron 202 by Wilmaset, Birkenhead, Wirral.
Printed in England by Jolly and Barber Ltd., Rugby, Warwickshire.
Bound by Mackays of Chatham, Kent.
Colour separations by Jolly and Barber Ltd.
Covers printed by Belmont Press Ltd., Northampton.

Acknowledgements

This book represents a simple but wide-ranging introduction to a subject which is labyrinthine in complexity. Inevitably I have leaned heavily on the generosity and friendship of a number of specialists with whom I have been fortunate enough to work on the making of the television film series *Discovering Animals*. In particular, I should like to record my appreciation to: Eric Ashby, Michael Clark, Jock Cockburn, Tony and Anne Cook, Frederick Courtier, Maurice Gosling, Stephen Harris, David MacDonald, Leo Harrison Matthews, Pat Morris, Ernest Neal, Judy Rowe, Bob Stebbings, Mike Stoddart, Kenneth Whitehead, Huw Davies and Jennie Allen. Hilary Soper and Nicki Holford improved what Richard Mabey once called my 'radioprose' by inserting full stops and paragraph pauses. Remaining errors are all my own work.

This is a suitable place to record my warm appreciation of farmer John Martin, who allows me to trample along his Devon hedgerows. And my gratitude to Neil Nightingale, Theo Cockerell, Suzi Miller, Hugh Tasman, Mandy Leith, Erica Griffiths and Bryn Brooks, who all neglected their families in order to make the films. And to offer a delicate bouquet to Sheila Innes, who made it all possible. Thank you.

Tony Soper

First published 1985
Published by The British Broadcasting Corporation
35 Marylebone High Street,
London W1M 4AA

ISBN 0 563 21087 7 (paperback)
ISBN 0 563 21204 7 (hardback)

CONTENTS

INTRODUCTION

Forty-one mammals are native to the British Isles, excluding the seals and whales which visit our shores. But if you add the mammals which have been introduced from other countries and the domesticated animals which have gone wild, you can bring the list up to sixty. That may not sound very impressive when you know that there are some four thousand species of mammals known to science, but ours are small islands and our mammals enrich them.

Over the years we have lost our wolves, bears, boars and beavers; grey squirrels, wallabies, mink and Mongolian gerbils are a poor exchange. But they are all enjoyable in their different ways. The complex social relationships and lifestyles of our mammals provide a lifetime of fascination for anyone who seeks to know them.

The mammal class is characterised by great diversity of form and function and this is well shown even by our relatively impoverished British list, with members which vary in size from the pigmy shrew to the magnificent red deer. Most of them are small and inconspicuous, but as members of the same class they share the typical mammalian features. They have hairy bodies and large brains, they are warm-blooded and they have mammary glands. No other animals have mammary glands which secrete milk for the nourishment of their young. The facility of rearing young on the mother's milk allows mammals, including man, to give birth at any time of the year, provided that there is an adequate supply of food for the mothers. Warm-bloodedness – the ability to maintain a more-or-less constant body temperature – makes it possible for mammals to live in climates which at first sight seem inhospitable, from mountain tops to the polar regions.

Their large brains have enabled mammals to enjoy the fruits of evolutionary success. Rightly or wrongly, we regard ourselves as belonging to the most important grouping, in which we naturally classify ourselves as the pinnacle of achievement. It was Professor Harrison Matthews, the distinguished ex-Director of the London Zoo, who pointed out that it was a mere hiccup in evolution which opened the way for mammals to take over the world at a time when it was touch-and-go that the birds might take the prize. In the event they have taken mastery of the air and many of us would argue that they are of near status and interest!

Mammals tend to be creatures of habit, but they are adaptable and have insinuated themselves into most corners of Britain, very often living in close community with Man. Yet they are mostly creatures of the dusk, dawn and night with good reason, and they are experts at concealment. It is easy for them to be out of sight, out of mind, even though they are literally our neighbours.

They live in a world of smells which is radically different from the one we know ourselves. (Perhaps the popularity of bird watching depends to a large extent on the fact that birds mostly live in a daylight world of sight and sound which is familiar to us, even though birds are far removed from us in evolutionary terms.) But fortunately, some of the mammals are thorough-going day

As social animals, wolves were potential candidates for domestication, but they are not easy to tame.

creatures, and most of them show their faces to the light at some time, so it is possible, with a certain amount of effort, to get to know them a little. And even if you don't manage to see them, they leave a variety of messages in a variety of ways from which we can learn a lot about their lives.

Wild animals have a healthy respect for us. They avoid detection if possible and they avoid close contact, because they fear the gun. They blend into their background with a facility which defies us, making observation difficult. But there are some simple practical rules for mammal-watching. First, learn the geography of your target-area, for that will tell you what kind of animals are likely to be there. Talk to the landowners and land-workers for sometimes (though not always) they will know what is about. Try to talk to naturalists by way of local societies and the meetings of your County Trust (for details see page 140). And when you go into the field, whether it is your local park or railway embankment or the wild woods, wear suitable clothes. Dress in non-crackling materials which are coloured in drab browns and greens. It is a positive disadvantage to buy the sort of mock camouflage clothes often on sale in ex-army shops. Quite apart from the fact that they make you conspicuous in almost any group of people, they are not suited to our countryside. The mammal-watcher must try hard to be invisible! Your pink pale face and hands are glaringly obvious to your animal quarry and if you are going to be serious about the job you must find a way of covering these too.

When you are correctly dressed, the next most important rule is to move slowly and aim always to merge into the background. 'Going for a walk' and mammal-watching are two quite different activities. It may be best not to move at all, but to establish yourself in a hide, overlooking likely country at the right time of day. You can buy camouflage netting (see page 140) but a few bales of straw do a good job; it is even better to use local materials, making a hidey-hole from the prevailing reeds or foliage. But try not to cut or slash too much branch-bending makes more sense and causes less disruption.

It is, of course, of the utmost importance that we do not disturb and disrupt the lives of the animals we seek to know. Our inter-relationship is real, so we have a right to learn about them, but it is as well to remember that in our long history we have abused and exploited them shamelessly. In every walk of life our activities influence theirs, for better or for worse. We claim to 'love' them, but perhaps developing an element of respect would be more satisfactory.

Human beings started with an admirably close relationship with nature, as hunter-gatherers who lived in ecological harmony. Since those far-off days we have become farmers, subjugating animals to our requirements to the extent that our relationship is now as agro-industrialists; as consumers we barely know the species we are eating, let alone its individuality.

A long time ago we parcelled up the land into 'ownership', with a sublime disregard to the rights of the other non-human inhabitants. To add insult to injury we have increased our numbers so that we invade every nook and cranny of the landscape.

Our hope for the future has to be the growing movement in favour of a wildlife conservation which recognises that all organisms play their part in our system, and that they are all entitled to a fair share of the space and the bounty.

A useful first step towards that desirable goal is a better understanding of the requirements of wild animals. This book aims to be a simple introduction to the lifestyles of one important group, with an emphasis on the ways in which we might get closer, both literally and philosophically.

Tony Soper

Scientific classification

Scientific names are allotted to all living things according to the *Linnaean system* which classifies them in terms of family relationships. The end result is a unique name for every 'kind' of life. Plants and animals are represented by two kingdoms. The Animal Kingdom is subdivided into phyla – branches – one of which encompasses the vertebrates, the animals with backbones. The vertebrates are further divided into a number of classes, one of which is for the mammals; in turn the mammal class is divided into orders. Orders are major groupings (carnivores, for example, form one order) and they are further subdivided into families. Within the family, a group of closely related mammals with common traits of behaviour or pelage or body structure represent a genus, which is finally divided into species, the 'kinds' of animal which we recognise as separate. By definition a species consists of individuals which group together to form a viable breeding stock and whose offspring reproduce true; that is,

they are reproductively isolated from other groups.

So each mammal is known by its generic name followed by its specific name, so that a mole is the species *Talpa europae*. It belongs to the Family Talpidae which is part of the Order of Insectivores of the Mammal Class of the Chordate Phylum of the Animal Kingdom.

Latin is used as the language of classification because, being a dead language, its words are not subject to the subtle changes of time and common usage. In Britain the terms wood mouse and long-tailed field mouse are freely used to identify one and the same animal, and doubtless the living languages of the world would extend the list to cover several pages. But this animal can be identified unequivocally by its one scientific name *Apodemus sylvaticus* with no possibility of misunderstanding anywhere in the world. The diagram below shows the system at work in classifying a weasel.

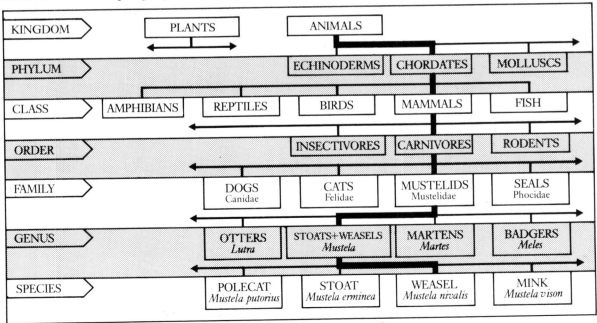

1
HEDGEHOGS, MOLES, SHREWS

Insectivora

There are three British families in the scientific group or Order known as insectivores; hedgehogs, moles and shrews. They are all primitive animals which have gone through little evolutionary change in fifty million years. Their design must be very effective – it works, and has stood the test of time.

Hedgehogs

Of all the wild animals in the three insectivore families, hedgehogs are the best known. There may be badgers at the bottom of the garden, foxes under the shed and deer eating the roses at dawn, but judging from my postbag the animal which people see most often in the garden and show most interest in is the hedgehog. Sadly, we also see them as flattened remains on our roads, but that at least is an indication of their numbers, for the carnage seems to continue unabated. Unfortunately for the hedgehog, its response to danger is not to run away but to stand still or adopt its defensive posture, rolled up in a ball and protected by its sharp spines. In spite of suggestions that they are learning to run when cars bear down on them, there is no doubt that any such change in their behaviour will evolve slowly and they will continue to suffer the consequences of their current behaviour.

Ironically they are relying on defensive equipment which is actually highly effective for its job of discouraging would-be predators. The spines are in fact modified hairs, replacing the more usual mammal fur on all of the upper surfaces of the animal except its face. There are several thousand of these. In a relaxed attitude they lie back and can be stroked without pain, but specialised back muscles will erect them if necessary until they offer the equivalent of a barbed-wire fence to any aggressor. If this doesn't warn off the intruder, then the animal tucks its head down and under its body, arches its back as the fore and hind parts are pulled together and rolls into a prickly ball which defeats all but the most determined assault.

The hedgehog has real need of its protection, for it represents a hearty meal to a predator. Fortunately, the spines do a good job and hedgehogs lead a relatively secure life, although the occasional individual may fall prey to a fox or badger. A hedgehog skin neatly turned inside out and eaten clean is the work of a badger. But their most dangerous enemy is definitely man and his motor car. Although hedgehog meat is said to be very good, the gypsies who baked them (wrapped in mud, over a camp fire) can never have been a serious threat to their populations.

One of the things people always seem to know about hedgehogs is that they are infested with fleas. This is probably because they can be seen so easily through the spiny thicket and coarse body hair which parts easily for a clear view of the skin. But although the fleas are there, they do not represent a threat to us. There are dozens of different species of British flea, but most of them are designed to enjoy the particular habitat offered

Hedgehogs are welcome visitors to the garden, eating the slugs and snails and leaving you your lettuces.

by a particular host, i.e. they are *host-specific*. So hedgehog fleas are hedgehog fleas, dog fleas are dog fleas, and they don't mix freely. They may try a different host for a trial period but soon drop off in the presence of a more suitable home.

Hedgehogs live in open country, not specially in hedgerows, such as open farmland, woodland edge, suburban gardens and parks, cemeteries, railway embankments and so on. They don't like wet or marshy places, and like to be near the sort of cover which provides them with shelter where they can lie up, breed and hibernate. They are not great travellers; radio tracking has shown that they might cover a mile or two in a night, only working further afield if food is hard to come by. They do not defend a territory but forage as they see fit, meeting other hedgehogs on their perambulations only by chance, for they are not sociable animals.

Although we often see them trundling about the flower borders in a leisurely kind of way, their short legs are perfectly capable of lifting their bodies well clear of the ground and running at what we would regard as a brisk walking pace. The action almost matches that of the Citroen cars which can vary their clearance in response to road conditions.

Their hearing is excellent, and their well developed senses of smell and touch make up for poor eyesight. (It is the vibration of the road rather than the oncoming headlights which triggers the rolling-up response.) They find their food by random search rather than by active hunting. Earthworms, woodlice, snails and invertebrate food of all kinds are eaten, as well as frogs, toads, lizards and even small birds and mammals up to the size of a very young rabbit. They commonly dig out mouse nests to eat the young. Bees and wasps can be tackled whole without ill effect and they are said to be able to battle it out with a snake, even the adder which is quite capable of killing a hedgehog if it could only find a way past the spines to bite the body. For all that, the hedgehog approaches cautiously before the final dash, spines erect and teeth poised for the kill.

Certainly they prefer meat, though they will take vegetable food, including fruit, berries and nuts. One of the oldest of folk tales about the hedgehog is that 'when he findeth apples on the earth he rowleth himselfe uppon them, until he have filled all his prickles . . . so forthe he goeth, makyng a noyse like a cart wheel' (*Historie of Fourefooted Beastes*, Edward Topsell, 1607). The naturalist Maurice Burton researched many examples and showed that it was perfectly possible

for hedgehogs to transport apples on their backs, and there is no doubt that they enjoy eating them. Indeed, the gypsies believe that hedgehog meat is at its best during the apple season. Burton also showed that there was a lot of truth in the old saying that hedgehogs take advantage of the milk offered by cows, and that this is by no means confined to the drips which spill because of a full bag; the animals make active efforts to draw milk from the teat.

There is even less doubt about the hedgehog's enthusiasm for the eggs of ground-nesting birds. Biting with their canine teeth, they open or crush a hole large enough to allow them to lick out the yolk. Eggs from a sand dune ternery may provide a major source of food during the breeding season. Hedgehogs certainly make raids on domestic fowls, and have been seen to shove a partridge off her eggs while the outraged bird tried to beat it off with her wings. They tackle well grown pullets and young gulls, sitting on their backs to chew at the tail end.

Hedgehogs are unsociable, solitary creatures. Even in the breeding season, the sexes meet only for a short period of courtship. In May or June the two animals come together with a show of apparent reluctance. The male circles round the female on a grassy arena, the female turning her back on the male who perseveres in pressing his suit. It is a noisy affair involving a certain amount of rhythmic snorting and puffing. Eventually she submits, though there may have been several previous sessions which came to nothing. She adopts a posture which flattens her spines in a helpful manner, as the male mounts her with understandable caution.

Hedgehogs go in for some curious antics which may be mistaken for courtship. In one performance, a single individual runs around and around in a circle as if he were in a circus ring. This may go on for many minutes or even an hour, and be repeated on subsequent nights. It is certainly not a courtship activity, since no other animal is involved, but whether it is evidence of illness or caused by some form of pesticide pollution, is not yet known.

Once successfully impregnated, the female is left to her own devices by the male who plays no further part in family life. She builds a sheltered nursery nest, gathering leaves and grasses in her mouth to construct a large ball of material which she sites somewhere offering a measure of security, such as under a bramble bush, shed or log pile. After a gestation period of about four and

Hedgehogs are born blind. The first soft spines grow from 'pimples', but are soon moulted as the prickly ones grow through.

a half weeks, the young are born blind and spineless in June or July. The first white spines quickly develop from pimples, but are soon moulted to reveal characteristic brown spines which begin to grow within a day or two of birth. The average litter is of four or five. If the family is disturbed within the first day or so the mother will eat her young, thus absorbing energy which might fuel a second attempt at breeding, but if the disturbance occurs at a later stage she will simply carry the young away and make another nest. If all goes well, the young are suckled in the nest. Their eyes open at two weeks, and after three weeks they leave the nursery to follow their mother and learn to snuffle for food, returning to the nest for milk. Weaned by six weeks, the family party breaks up and the young disperse. In all this the father plays no part at all, beyond fertilising the female.

Hedgehogs eat large quantities of garden pests like insect larvae, slugs, snails and beetles. It is possible to get a great deal of pleasure by putting out food for the animals and persuading them to make regular summer evening visits to a feeding station at a place where you may conveniently watch the action. At first, put a saucer of bread and milk in a corner which is in only just enough light for you to see from inside the house. Put it close to cover so that the hog doesn't have to venture far into the open. Initially, the animals will be reluctant to show themselves. But persevere, and soon you will be able to move the food, bit by bit, to a more convenient viewing position where the hedgehog will accept a more illuminated dinner. Be careful not to surprise him by sudden movements, door-openings or curtain-drawing. After a few weeks he will be bomb-proof.

Bread and milk is the traditional food to offer hedgehogs although it is sometimes suggested that milk is not good for them. But Pat Morris, a zoologist at Royal Holloway College in London who probably knows more about hedgehogs than anyone else in Britain, has found no proof that it is harmful, especially if it is diluted. He points out that milk itself is not actively harmful under any circumstances, and there is no doubt that the hedgehogs love it. In fact Pat had one captive hedgehog that would only eat earthworms if they had first been dipped in milk! The probability is that milk offers a most useful supplement to the natural diet, and, as we shall see, it can be a life-saver in the autumn.

Water is an important requirement for your hedgehogs, as it is for many other garden visitors and residents. If you have a pond (and this is a highly desirable addition to any wildlife garden), do be sure that there is an easy way out for hedgehogs which fall in. Many hedgehogs drown each year after finding themselves in a pond with slippery plastic sides. They climb well, but need something to get a grip on. So have a ramp of some kind, or lay a scrambling net of chicken wire down the side. The British Hedgehog Preservation Society (address on page 140) have done sterling work in providing exit ramps from the cattle grids which annually trap many hedgehogs to a prison where they starve to death.

In times of drought, hedgehogs will be grateful for a water supply, and it is at this time that they will also be glad of extra food, since worms and insects may be hard to come by. As in bird table feeding, the important thing is to offer as great a variety as possible, but even so, you may find that they are only seriously interested in bread and milk.

Hedgehogs climb well, and unless you have an outsize wall they will wander freely in and out of your garden. Indeed, they need to be able to forage over a fairly wide area, as the home range diagram indicates (page 18). They will climb a 2 metre wire netting fence with ease, and often enough will take the easy way down hill, tumbling over with spines erect in order to break their fall. So 'your' hedgehog, which comes to feed at intervals at dusk and into the night, is most likely a whole series of individuals which call to visit as part of their several itineraries.

It often happens that hedgehogs produce a second brood of young, perhaps because the first brood was born early in the summer, or came to a sticky end. Whatever the reason, the progeny of the autumn brood may not have enough time to accumulate the fat reserves, laid down in the neck and shoulders, which are needed to support them through the lean times of winter. If you find a young hedgehog in October, it may well be in need of help. The question is simply whether it has enough fat to keep itself alive through the hibernation period, and the answer is equally simply obtained. You weigh the animal. If it weighs more than 450 g, it is ready to hibernate. If not, its chances of finding enough wild food to reach that figure are very slim. At this point you would consider the possibility of keeping it in temporary captivity in order to fatten it beyond the magic figure.

If you decide to take the young hog under your wing, first dust it well with pyrethrum flea powder (unless it is very young), avoiding the eyes. The autumn orphans are perhaps best kept in an orange box, tipped on its side and made secure with netting, in a garage or shed. Give them plenty of newspaper and hay on a peat bed, providing a packed box into which they burrow. An exceptionally young hog may even need a hot waterbottle. Offer a variety of food, since in the wild they are used to a diverse diet (bread and milk is certainly not enough for a captive hedgehog). Scraps from the Sunday joint, biscuit, mince, fresh liver, scrambled egg etc, almost everything is grist to their mill. Slightly sloppy puppy meal is good, but do not offer fishy catfood. The animal's droppings should be checked to make sure they are black and fairly firm. Sloppy faeces are the result of sloppy meals and to be discouraged. Too much bread and milk will reveal green sloppy faeces, even more to be discouraged!

Once the animal is comfortably past the 450 g barrier, it should be released, preferably in mild dry weather, in good time for the November hibernation. Hibernation is a strategy developed by a number of mammals as a way of solving the problems of food shortage. Although it is normally associated with winter, it may happen at any time when food becomes hard to get, in any extremes of weather. But of course the animal must have reserves of body fat in order to survive. And, conversely, the animal won't hibernate at all if it doesn't have to. It is not a state of sleep, but a way of reducing energy requirements so that the stored fat is enough to keep the body alive – just – until food becomes available again. In this state of near suspended animation, the hedgehog's body temperature falls from the normal 35°C to around 10°C, in sympathy with its surroundings. The heartbeat reduces, breathing almost ceases. The animal simply shuts off power and lies still, conserving energy. In its winter nest it lies rolled up, safe and secure, but not warm, since warmth would stimulate activity which could not be sustained.

As the days shorten and the evenings draw in, hedgehogs resort to brambly or scrubby places where they prepare to construct a winter nest. They may go into the shrubbery or under a shed, up against a fence, into the compost heap or under a log pile, but wherever they go they like to be *under* something. They gather plenty of leaves, bracken and grasses, and build a ball of material which is held in place by the brambles or vegetation of the site. In much the same way as a broody bird forms a nest cup by turning round and shuffling the materials so that they become compacted and tidy, the hedgehog burrows into the middle of its bundle and creates a comfortable ball-shaped chamber. This interior is well insulated and stable, maintaining a temperature which is relatively unaffected by outside extremes of winter cold or even warmth, but most importantly it offers shelter from the danger of freezing.

While the summer nests may have been occupied by several animals – the mother and her family – the winter nest is prepared for the sole use of one hedgehog, rolled up into a ball, with its nose and legs tucked away into the warm fur of its underside, the prickly skin enveloped in a cocoon of leaves.

The availability of suitable winter nest sites and a generous supply of dry leaves may be an important factor in determining hedgehog distribution. Suitable nest sites in a garden may be more important than the free supply of bread and milk in making it attractive to hedgehogs. So you may feel it worthwhile to offer the equivalent of a bird's nesting-box to tempt the prickly urchin.

One way of doing this involves the old-fashioned terra-cotta pots used for forcing rhubarb. Laid on their sides at a shallow angle to the ground (for good drainage) with the narrow end downmost and the wide end sealed with a piece of tough plastic, this has worked on an experimental basis. It would be good to have some more comments on its effectiveness.

A well-tried and moderately successful box has been developed and improved through the years by the Henry Doubleday Research Association (see right). One of its characteristics is that it can be produced quite cheaply and effectively by even the most clumsy handyman as long as he can manage to wield a hammer, saw and brace and bit. (See page 141 for the address to write to for further details.)

The wood can be purchased either rough-sawn or ready-planed. The former is obviously cheaper. You may also be able to obtain some of the wood from a demolition site. One word of advice: although you might be tempted to creosote the house to protect it from the weather, if you do so you will certainly not attract your hedgehogs. They don't seem to like even the faintest smell of either creosote or paint. For preference untreated wood should be used, although if you do need to

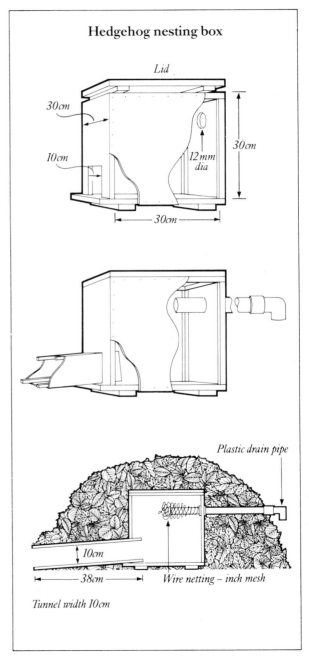

Hedgehog nesting box

Lid

30 cm

10 cm

12 mm dia

30 cm

30 cm

Plastic drain pipe

10 cm

38 cm

Wire netting – inch mesh

Tunnel width 10 cm

use something then the wood should be treated with clear Cuprinol.

Place the box in a carefully chosen and undisturbed part of the garden, perhaps in a shrubbery or well-grown border, so that some of the site-criteria listed above are achieved. Cover it with a sheet of heavy polythene, making sure that the ventilator is not obstructed, and submerge it under a mound of soil. No one has yet discovered a sure way of leading hedgehogs to discover these highly desirable winter homes, so it is a hit-and-miss affair, but well worth trying. A piece of bacon rind in the entrance tunnel has been

suggested to tempt them to explore, but there will be several other creatures equally happy to eat the bacon. Be sure that there's plenty of suitable dry bedding material close by.

All being well, your winter guest will emerge, bleary-eyed, sometime after mid-February. The male, mature at one year, will become fertile in April, ready to serve the female when he encounters her, when she comes on heat in May, and the merry-go-round turns again. To celebrate the happy event, you might clean out and de-bug the winter quarters with pyrethrum, and air the box in readiness for the onset of another winter.

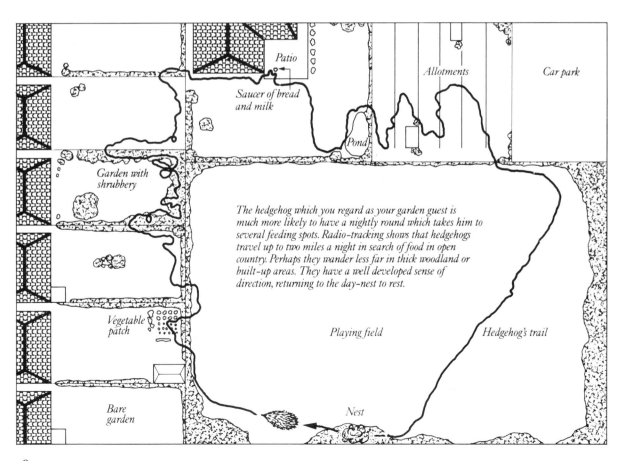

Patio

Saucer of bread and milk

Allotments

Car park

Pond

Garden with shrubbery

The hedgehog which you regard as your garden guest is much more likely to have a nightly round which takes him to several feeding spots. Radio-tracking shows that hedgehogs travel up to two miles a night in search of food in open country. Perhaps they wander less far in thick woodland or built-up areas. They have a well developed sense of direction, returning to the day-nest to rest.

Vegetable patch

Playing field

Hedgehog's trail

Bare garden

Nest

Moles

Moles are usually less welcome visitors than hedgehogs, at least for the lazy gardener. The work of one mole in one night – for they don't work in gangs – can turn your lawn into a battlefield. However, although a chain of molehills may disfigure your close-cut sward, the material is easily dispersed, and it has to be said that the well-loosened soil is excellent for potting. And have patience; once an underground tunnel system has been completed the mole will rest from his labours. Provided a good supply of worms drops in, the animal won't need to throw up any more hills.

Moles are master-tunnellers. Put one on the lawn and he will disappear underground in a quarter of a minute, provided the conditions are sympathetic, offering soft warm soil. Even in hard clay it will be out of sight in a minute. In top gear it can shift just under 6 kg of soil in twenty minutes.

Molehills are simply the spoil heaps resulting from tunnel operations, in which the mole constructs runways a few inches underground and parallel with the surface. The mole tunnels with its forepaws, pushing the soil behind it, and forges ahead. But at intervals it digs a vertical tunnel up to the surface, in order to clear away the spoil which now blocks the tunnel behind it. It pushes the spoil out by shoving with a forepaw, not by heaving with its broad shoulders as the old natural history books will tell you. We now know exactly what happens as a result of research in which moles were observed demonstrating their technique in glass-sided earth-boxes.

Once the tunnel system has been established, the mole patrols it periodically to gather the worms which 'drop in'. In firm clay the tunnels will be more or less permanent, but in loose sandy soil there will be a constant requirement for new tunnelling.

By choice, moles are animals of deciduous woodland (conifer woodland offers acid soil and therefore a poor population of worms). But although they are more numerous in woods they are not so conspicuous and it is easy to think of them as animals of open pastureland because in this habitat their presence is so much more obvious. In fact the open field molehills are often made by inexperienced sub-adults which are denied access to the long-established woodland territory held by older individuals.

The spoil heaps are associated with deep runs. Another burrowing activity produces ridges which betray shallow tunnels made when the mole 'swims' by breast stroke just under the surface.

This activity is typical in freshly ploughed and harrowed fields where the going is easy. Such ridge runs may also be made early in the summer morning after rain, and allow the mole easy pickings of small worms and insect larvae.

Moles spend more time underground than any other British mammal. They do show their faces on the surface occasionally, though we are very lucky to see them. On a warm moist night in summer, for example, when earthworms tend to lie mating on a grassy surface, moles will emerge to forage above the ground. Worms are their main and preferred diet, especially in the winter. Only at a time of drought, when worms are relatively inactive, will moles be seen more frequently at the surface, searching for insects and grubs. In hard weather moles may dig deeper, making new tunnels in search of the worms which have migrated downwards to avoid dessication. So molehills may appear even while snow is on the ground. In fact winter is a good time for molehill watching. Grass is shorter, and cereal crops are close to the ground rendering the hills more conspicuous. Moles are active right through the winter and do not hibernate.

You will be lucky to see a mole actually at work, but a good tip is to keep a sharp eye open for a blackbird or thrush which will be following mole operations closely. If the molehill volcano is active then the bird will stand by hoping for the odd insect to be unwillingly thrown up in the spoil. Watch carefully and there is always the chance you may catch a glimpse of the velvet face and long insectivore snout.

The mole's cylindrical body is made for running along tunnels. There are no awkward appendages such as ear flaps or bushy tails. But it has forepaws which are built like spades, with five long, strong-pointed claws. Its foreparts are powerfully muscular, the shoulder held well forward on the body so that the tunnelling limbs are efficiently served. The back feet and limbs are nothing like

Top: Mole-catcher John Tatlow begins his work excavating a mole fortress.
Centre: A 60-cm deep trench is dug around the hill.
Bottom: Nine runs into the hill are exposed, including one at the very top.

*Top: The runs are injected with polyurethane foam.
Centre and bottom: The extensive tunnel system inside
the fortress is revealed.*

so powerful, and their main function is to act as bracing struts, holding the body firm against the tunnel.

On the face and chin, and along the edge of the front feet, there are sensitive hairs which provide tactile information. The mole has a poor sense of smell and poor sight, but the tiny eyes are not by any means useless. Quite apart from anything else, they provide daylight and daylength information which is probably important in determining the onset of breeding.

The mole lives a solitary life in his tunnel complex, though some of the major routes may be shared with neighbours. A well-established system may involve 40 or 50 metres of tunnelling and an average home range is about 400 square metres.

Although moles may share tunnels, they are not neighbourly by nature. They are not only solitary, but aggressively so. Although they probably prefer to avoid contact, if they do meet another mole they square up for an immediate fight. Males and females are equally aggressive, and though, like most fights among wild animals of the same species, the contests are short, sharp and conclusive with one contestant running away to fight another day, there are recorded cases of fights to the death. The mole is fiercely territorial and he fights in defence of his own patch.

In spring the courtship and mating of moles seem to be a fleeting affair. The male tunnels to enter a female's territory and to pair, after which both parties immediately resume their pugnacious ways.

The female builds a ball-shaped nest from hay and leaves, most often oak leaves. In the case of the traditional woodland mole, the nest will very likely be associated with the base of a tree which communicates with the long-established tunnel feeding system. In open pastureland the nest may be at or above ground level, and lies inside the 'fortress', a particularly large molehill as much as 0.6 metres high and 2.4 metres across.

On average there is only one litter of four young born in April or early May after a gestation period of about a month. The young are born naked and with red skins, which soon change first to pink and then to black. Their soft dense fur begins to grow at about two weeks, their almost obsolete eyes open at three weeks. By the time they are a month old they are beginning to explore the tunnel system. Suckled until at most five weeks, they are then driven off by their mother to leave the home tunnels and find their own place to dig, probably within half a mile of their birthplace.

May or June is the time when you are most likely to catch a glimpse of a mole. It will almost certainly be one of these innocent half-grown juveniles, crossing a road or making surface runs in the grass or newly turned soil. This is because at this stage the young, but already independent mole will live above ground while it searches for a likely tunnelling-ground of its own. At this time it will be vulnerable to traffic accidents, to say nothing of tawny owls, foxes and cats.

Man has always been a major predator on moles. Moleskins made fashionable waistcoats for nineteenth-century gentlemen and at one time something like a million skins were marketed annually. But the major reason why moles are trapped and poisoned in astonishing numbers nowadays is because they are regarded as a pest by most farmers. Their surface burrowings disturb the roots of seedling plants and stunt them; the hills offer an ideal seed-bed for colonising weeds and thus begin a degradation of the pasture. If the hills are allowed to stand, then rabbits use them as latrines, they sprout vegetation and become consolidated, and may be adopted by ants. So farmers harrow the hills and curse the moles which are unaffected by the loss of their molehills. Nowadays trappers are rare, and control is mainly by use of strychnine.

Moles are well equipped for digging. Their forepaws act as spades.

Digging into warm soft soil a mole can be underground in fifteen seconds. When tunnelling, it digs with its forepaws, then pushes the soil behind in order to forge ahead. At intervals it digs a vertical tunnel and pushes the spoil out to form the 'hill'.

Once the tunnel system has been established, the mole patrols it in order to gather the worms which have dropped in. It is only in the unfavourable conditions of drought that they are forced to the surface in search of the less favoured insects and grubs.

When food is abundant moles will store the surplus, biting the worm at the head end to incapacitate but not kill it.

Shrews

Shrews are closely related to moles and have similar short, dense and soft fur. But instead of being entirely black they tend to be darker above and lighter below. They have the give-away pointed snout, ears that are only just visible and small eyes.

Shrews are most often seen as pathetic little dead bodies in pathways, rejected as potential food by almost everything that has passed. They are abundant, yet unappreciated by the weasels and domestic cats which might be expected to find them nice bite-sized morsels. It seems that they just taste awful, a defence strategy that works some of the time, although to judge by the behaviour of our house cats it doesn't save them from being killed, merely from being *eaten*. Shrews have flank glands which produce a strong musky smell which is presumably used in marking territory and in mating, and perhaps this musk provides the clue to the shrew's unpalatability. Also some shrew species make poisonous saliva, another product for the testing ground of natural selection on the road to a defence technique. Nevertheless, our common shrews are taken freely by owls as an important item in their diet, so presumably it is really just a question of each to its own taste.

Like the other insectivores, shrews are unsociable creatures, quick to fight when they meet others of their kind. The musky smells presumably aid the delicate process of joining together in mating by delivering a message which avoids the usual reaction of an offering to fight.

Shrews live short lives at a ferocious pace, hunting invertebrate food and eating more than their body weight of this each day. They move restlessly and excitedly, but alternate periods of activity with periods of relaxation. They have acute hearing, smell and touch, so probably it is their sight which is least important sense to them. They are very vocal, but their high-pitched squeakings are above our range of hearing.

Common shrew

The common shrew enjoys alder groves, water
meadows and damp woodland, but is abundant in
almost any habitat provided there is plenty of
cover at ground level. It nests in abandoned mouse
burrows or other underground holes, making a
nursery from grasses and moss, and lining it with
leaves. The nest is often at ground level, but under
the cover of matted vegetation or fallen bark or
branches. There may be four or five litters a year,
with anything up to ten young. Born blind and
naked, the young will be weaned at three weeks,

Common shrews are solitary animals, living in a system of underground and surface runs.

fully grown at six. Progeny of the earliest litter may be sexually mature at twelve weeks and may even breed in their first summer, but normally in the following spring. Few survive to breed a second year.

One of the more joyous sights of nature is to see a family of shrews 'caravanning' away from the nest at weaning-time. Led by their mother, each young grips the base of the tail of the animal in front, and they then snake along in line-astern as if they were a single organism.

Pygmy shrew

The smallest of all our mammals is the pygmy shrew. It has a proportionately longer tail than the common shrew and there is less contrast between the colour of its back and its flanks. Ranging over a territory some 30 metres square this animal spends more time on the surface than the common shrew and is also more active by day. It is widely distributed over Britain, except for islands like Shetland and the Channel Islands, and it lives almost anywhere so long as there is plenty of ground cover.

The pygmy shrew is less abundant than the common shrew, but has a similar lifestyle.

Water shrew

At least the water shrew is reasonably easy to identify, with its typical shrew nose and its black upper parts. It lives in or near fresh water – ditches, ponds and streams – and while the other shrews are all perfectly able to swim and do so at will, the water shrew is specially adapted for the job, with stiff fringes of hair on its feet to provide a paddle-blade effect. The tail has fringes of stiff hair along its sides which allow it to act as a control surface, i.e. as a rudder. It swims and dives readily, with a vigorous kicking motion in the underwater chase. Water beetles, spiders, caddis larvae, fish eggs and tadpoles, newts, etc are all on its menu. Captured prey is taken ashore to be eaten. It also takes earthworms and small voles.

The underground nests are approached by way of a tunnel with an underwater entrance, in the style of a beaver.

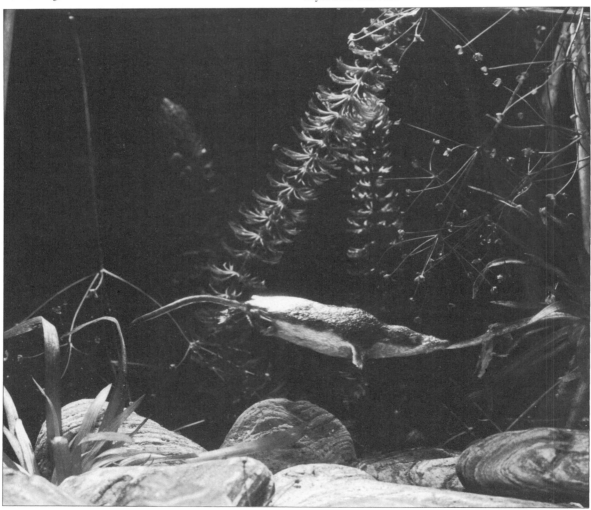

Water shrews kick out vigorously in the underwater chase for diving beetles. Although adapted for underwater work they may well be found in scrub or woodland miles from the water. Their saliva glands produce a poisonous secretion which paralyses large prey such as voles.

White-toothed shrews

Remote islands tend to be inhabited by their own shrew specialities. Two examples of this are the two species of white-toothed shrews in the British Isles; the likelihood is that they are here because of a chance introduction at some time in the past. Originating from south and central Europe, where they are still abundant, we have the lesser white-toothed shrew in the Isles of Scilly and the greater white-toothed shrew in the Channel Islands. Both are slightly smaller than the common shrew but have larger and more prominent foxy ears and long silky hairs on the tail. The fur is greyish or silver brown and the teeth, not surprisingly, are white, as distinct from all our other shrews which have red pigmentation on the teeth.

On Scilly, the lesser white-toothed, which may well not be a distinct sub-species at all, was first described in 1924. One place to find it is among the tideline detritus, especially where there is storm-tossed kelp. The kelp is collected and spread on fields as fertiliser, so it is not difficult to see how quickly this shrew could have spread through this group of islands, where it is still the only shrew.

The greater white-toothed shrew is found on the Channel Islands, where it was first recorded on Jersey and Sark in 1925; but only a dyed-in-the-wool shrew-watcher would be able to distinguish it from its close relative on Scilly.

2
BATS
Chiroptera

Chiroptera, the scientific name for bats, is Latin for 'hand wings' – the bats represent the only group of mammals capable of true, sustained, flight. They have extended finger bones which support double membranes of skin stretched between the fingers of the hand back to the foot and to the tail. They are nocturnal and navigate not so much by sight, as by sound, using their highly developed ears which serve as shortwave receptor 'dishes' for echo-location.

There are fifteen species of bat in Britain. And while they are fairly easy to see, they are not at all easy to identify, in flight or at rest. Much maligned, misunderstood and abused, they are also in decline. Their range is diminishing, their numbers falling. The greater horseshoe bat, for instance, is classified as rare and endangered, present in numbers that are perhaps only 2% of its population a century ago.

There are several reasons for this decline. Climatic variations have given us a series of summers which have provided a less generous supply of insects, their staple food. Agricultural changes have produced cleaner and tidier farmsteads which again produce fewer flying insects (one of the reasons why swallows too are less common now). The widespread use of insecticides has also reduced potential food supplies. Farmers and landowners are less tolerant of the sort of old trees which offer safe roosting places for bats, and disturbance of caves and renovation of old buildings has deprived them of roost places. And, sadly, the pest-controllers

who treat loft timbers for woodworm often kill them in their summer nurseries. The irony of this last reason for their decline is that the bats actually eat the wood-boring beetles.

People generally regard bats as unappealing creatures. On discovering that their house is lucky enough to have bats in the roof space, their first reaction is to demand that they should be exterminated. Bats suffer from an accumulation of ignorant myths. They are 'dirty, ugly, blind, tangle in your hair and are a health risk'. None of these is true, and bats badly need help to improve their image. They are actually harmless, sociable and highly intelligent. They are also decidedly useful as they have a great appetite for insects. And the chance of getting one tangled in your hair is negligible. One researcher tried – 'I put the bat in her hair and twisted the hair around and around, and then I let go, and out popped the bat like a cork from underwater'!

Church authorities often get an attack of bat-hatred when they discover that they really do have bats in their belfries. But far and away the best reaction is to rejoice in the good fortune. Enjoy their presence, don't regard them as a pest. They are, after all, no trouble. The droppings which they bestow so liberally dry to a non-corrosive powder which makes excellent insulation material. Or if you collect it it makes good fertiliser, as it is high in nitrogen, phosphorus and potassium. It is practically impossible to get rid of them anyway, except on a temporary basis. Probably the best plan is to cover

Long-eared bats are well named. They glide through foliage in pursuit of flies, moths and beetles.

the altar and pews etc, so that the droppings are not a nuisance, and to learn to live with your bats and love them as neighbours.

It is their roosting behaviour which most often brings us into close contact with bats, and this varies according to the season. In winter they look for natural and man-made caves in which to hibernate but in summer they prefer to be in the upper reaches of houses, farm buildings, churches and various industrial buildings where they are setting up their breeding colonies. Tree holes, hollows and crevices are also used, sometimes all the year. Bats can find their way in to a dry hollow in an old tree so long as there's a 1.5 cm crack offering access. Pollarded willows often make good bat roosts, and they have the advantage of being close to water, which in turn provides insects for their diet.

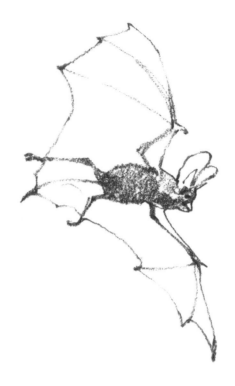

Contrary to their reputation as dirty beasts, bats are clean animals, and in choosing a summer breeding roost they positively prefer clean, more-or-less draught-free buildings, and do not like dust or cobwebs. So given the choice, they opt for the fresh rafting and timbers of a new house. And in fact newly built estates of houses attract bats very successfully. So please be delighted if you have bats in your belfry and don't think of having the sort of insecticidal treatment carried out which is in most cases totally unnecessary. Quite apart from anything else, it is an offence to kill a bat deliberately. In law it is an offence to intentionally damage, destroy or obstruct access to any place which a bat uses for shelter or protection, or to disturb a bat in residence. If for some reason you feel it is necessary to disturb a bat roost, you must consult the Nature Conservancy Council.

The largest roosts occur when pregnant females congregate in the nursery, in summer. Though mating will have occurred back in the previous autumn or even in the winter, delayed fertilisation of the egg ensures that the young will not be born till the high summer months when insects ought to be plentiful. Bats are slow to breed, not starting till anything up to their fourth year, and they do not necessarily breed every year. Also, they only have a single baby. So one way and another they are highly susceptible to population decline when unexpected factors militate against them.

The young bat is suckled for five weeks, though it is capable of flying at three. At dusk, the parents leave the juveniles in the nursery – a sort of crêche – while they hunt for food, returning several times to suckle their young. The bats are highly vulnerable to disturbance at this time, and if necessary the mother will carry her young off to another roost place, for bats tend to have a whole range of roosts which they use as required. At five weeks old the juvenile bat is weaned and

Bats often patrol a well defined flight-path in their search for flying insects. Different species exhibit different flight characteristics, some vigorous and powerful (noctules), some fluttering like butterflies (horseshoes). This long-eared bat can glide and hover.

independent, leaving the nursery to fend for itself. If it is exceedingly lucky, it might live to be thirty years old.

You may find injured or stunned bats lying on the ground, especially in high summer. These are usually young animals. Hang them up as near to the probable roost site as possible. At dusk the mother will emerge, react to the baby's call and gather it up. Late summer is a good time for bat-watching. Choose a slightly muggy evening which is noisy with the humming of insects. Sit where you have an uninterrupted view of a good patch of sky, and where you are near some trees or insect-rich scrub. If there is water nearby your chances are much increased. At dusk you will often see bats chasing flying insects over a river or waterside reedbeds. They enjoy parkland with permanent pasture of the sort which has escaped agricultural 'improvement', woodland, valleys with slow-moving rivers, meadows and marshland. They have a giant capacity for insects. A

pipistrelle, for instance, is said to take over 3500 in a night. The prey is taken in flight or picked off the ground, water or foliage.

Bats typically operate at dusk and through the night. Although they are not blind, as many people believe, they do not hunt by sight but by sound. Very early experiments showed that bats could fly blind but that they could not effectively catch prey when they were deaf. But it was only some fifty years ago that it was discovered that the high-pitched ultrasonic sounds they emit in flight provide a 'sound-picture' of their surroundings. By listening critically to the returning echoes of their own cries, the bats are able to detect flying insects and, just as important, avoid obstacles.

Untypically in mammals, bats do not have a steady body temperature. Their hunting temperature of 42°C is very much higher than our 37°C. But on returning to rest and starting a digestion period, the temperature falls by 10°, and in time it falls to match the temperature around it.

Bat wing shape and feeding niche

All 15 British species of bat feed on insects. These insects are sought after in different places depending on the way each bat flies. Wing shape tells us in which kind of habitat each bat feeds. Some bats such as the *noctules* and *Leisler's* have long, slender, pointed wings, which are ideal for fast, long-distance flight and rapid twisting to catch large beetles and moths flying high over the tree tops.

Serotines are also large bats which search out large insects, but their broad wings allow slow, cruising flight, then rapid turns and great manoeuvrability when chasing prey in the spaces between trees, such as in parkland. Often they swoop down from tree tops to pick up beetles emerging from grassland.

Pipistrelles, together with *whiskered* and *Brandt's bats*, have narrow, general-purpose wings, which are used to dart about, hunting small flies that swarm near or over hedgerows and bushes.

The equally small *lesser horseshoe bat* hawks crane flies which emerge from pastures and fly to bushes. The very wide wings allow this bat to fly close to the ground and slowly around the edges of shrubs.

Brown long-eared bats have similarly broad wings with round tips and these features, together with their supreme hearing, enable insects to be gleaned off foliage or branches. Long-eareds are able to hover whilst searching for food.

Greater horseshoe bats also have broad wings but this species exploits insects caught both low over pasture and within dense vegetation. They can fly quickly in the open or slowly amongst foliage.

Other species, such as *Daubenton's* and *barbastelles*, specialise in catching insects over water, while *Natterer's* feed along woodland edges rather like *mouse-eared bats*. *Bechstein's* emulate Long-eareds.

While each species has its feeding preferences, they all have to adapt rapidly in times of food shortage especially in bad weather.

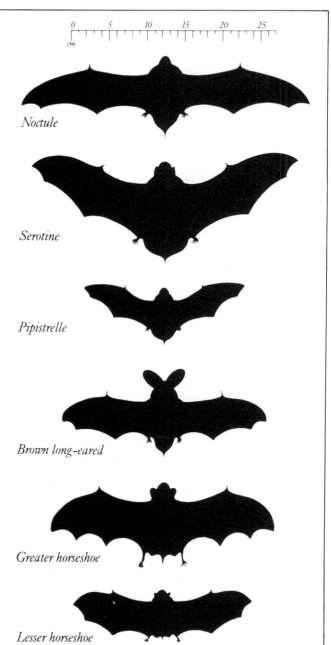

Noctule

Serotine

Pipistrelle

Brown long-eared

Greater horseshoe

Lesser horseshoe

At 16 days of age these baby hedgehogs have just opened their eyes. The second coat of dark spines is well formed and the animals are already able to curl up in a defensive ball. Within a week they will be leaving the nest for foraging trips with their mother and within a month they will be facing the world as individuals. But they will be grateful for an autumn saucer of bread and milk at dusk.

Moles seldom emerge from their tunnels (except for photographers!). Here you can see the broad spade-like fore-limbs which are such efficient diggers. Their velvety fur is unique in that it can actually move freely in any direction instead of just lying backwards as in other mammals, thus making it easy for the mole to move backwards in a tight-fitting tunnel. The naked snout is covered with delicate sensory organs which compensate for the mole's poor sight and hearing.

The large size and the black upperparts serve to
distinguish water shrews from other shrews. It is only
on the Scottish coast that you are likely to see one on
the seashore as in this photograph. In the rest of
Britain they are typically animals of freshwater
streams and ponds. The unpolluted water of watercress
beds suits them very well, and they enjoy the cover of
bankside vegetation.

*A long-eared bat fluttering among the oak leaves in
search of insects. Bats are the only mammals capable
of true flight. In fact this species collects much of its
food by picking off insects from the vegetation to which
it clings.*

Hares have longer ears than rabbits, and they are tipped with black. The legs are longer, too, associated with a loping gait. The eyes are set high in the head, allowing the hare to crouch low in its form, yet have good all-round vision to warn it of trouble. The brown hare pictured here is widely distributed in lowland Britain, mainly on farmland and rough pasture.

Red squirrels have large bushy tails. Their coats vary in colour from deep brown and rich chestnut to a greyish brown. The ear tufts are prominent only in winter. Conifer seeds or beech mast are their basic diet, but they are easily enticed to bird tables or will come indoors for peanuts.

Water voles are the size of rats but have much shorter tails, shorter ears and a blunter muzzle. They live by freshwater ponds, rivers, canals and ditches wherever there is a reasonable amount of bankside vegetation. They are expert swimmers and divers. Their normal food consists of grasses, but they will enjoy a share of your picnic sandwiches.

The common dormouse is not at all common. It lives in deciduous woodland, often in hedgerows and coppices, especially where there is a supply of hazelnuts, beech mast and sweet chestnuts. They are agile and active above ground most of the time, but strictly nocturnal and not at all easy to see. It is, however, possible to attract them to artificial nestboxes.

Like insectivorous birds, bats face the problem of winter food shortage. But instead of migration in search of sub-tropical or tropical insects, their strategy is that of the hedgehog – they hibernate. They increase their body weight by one third in the autumn, laying down a store of fat to see them through. Then from about October to April they hang it out in the winter roost. It follows that the winter roost is in a cold place such as a cave, where though the temperature is low the conditions are stable.

As hibernation time approaches the animals feed less frequently until they slip into a torpid

Pipistrelles chase small insects mostly, but can deal with a large catch by holding it in the tail pouch.

state where heart and pulse and breathing rate reduce to a level requiring very little energy to maintain. The body temperature then matches that of the surroundings, usually somewhere between 10° and 0°C, so that energy requirements are drastically reduced. The bat is not asleep, it is simply living at a very low energy level. If the ambient temperature increases it may move to another site. It may even emerge to fly in winter but this is a dangerous activity where prey consumed may amount to less than the energy expended. It is in winter that bats are so vulnerable to disturbance. If forced into activity, the fuel burned may reduce their resources to an inadequate level for survival. So bat-watching in winter is something which should be engaged in with great consideration and care.

As bats are finding it more and more difficult to find suitable roost places, it is a kindly gesture to provide potential sites for them. If you have a suitable roof or loft space, make sure there is an entrance hole. Or you might try fixing a piece of boarding to one of your walls by way of 20 mm battens, thus offering the sort of secret space bats might adopt. If the wood is warping, so much the better, since it will produce its own splits for access. Remember the seasonal requirements, summer warmth for nurseries, winter stability for hibernation, in choosing a site. Make sure there is some sun, but not too much.

Bat boxes make a change from tit boxes for the birds, and of course there is no reason why you should not offer both. Boxes can be bought, ready made, from the Fauna and Flora Preservation Society (address on page 140), but they are simple to make (see drawing on page 43).

Bat boxes offer the same facilities as do tit boxes, in other words they provide an alternative to a hole in a tree. But whereas tit boxes are used primarily for nesting, and may serve as roost boxes out of the breeding season, the function of the bat box is exactly the opposite. Although they might

Bats are often less gregarious in their hibernation quarters. Lesser horseshoe bats like to hang freely, their wings wrapped round their bodies so that they are completely covered.

be used for breeding, they are very much more likely to be used for straightforward roosting. And the other great difference from the conventional bird box is in the entrance hole. For the bats like to gain access by way of a slit at the bottom of the box.

The shape and size are not critical, but it is easiest and most convenient to build a bird box shape and the interior distance from front to back should not exceed 10 cm, for the bats enjoy a constricted space. Use rough-sawn and untreated 25 mm planking which you further roughen by making shallow horizontal sawcuts both inside and out (unlike birds, bats crawl about all over the box, both sides!). The entrance slit should be 15–20 mm wide and at least 50 mm long, better still the full width of the box. Do not treat it with preservatives. As for siting, generally speaking boxes which face south are used in spring and summer while those which face north are more likely to be used in autumn and winter. The height above ground is apparently not critical, say somewhere between 2 and 5 metres, but make sure there is a clear flight path to the landing, free of crowding branches and, if possible, shelter from prevailing winds.

If it is adopted, your bat box may offer a temporary home for anything up to fifty bats. Bob Stebbings at the Monkswood Experimental Research Station near Peterborough experimented with boxes in six different forests in the north of England and Scotland, putting up nearly 3,000 of them, eight boxes to a tree, in conifer plantations. Because the trees are carefully nurtured and felled before they get to the stage of deterioration which provides natural roost holes, the bats used the boxes enthusiastically, and in the course of his research he ringed 1,000 individuals.

As with bird boxes, the bat boxes are most likely to be used in places where there is a shortage of natural roost sites. It is easy to tell if they have been occupied, for there will be the characteristic blackish brownish droppings. If your box isn't adopted within about three years, move it and try again. If birds are perverse enough to find their way in, grin and bear it, clearing the nest away in autumn. But bear in mind that it has been known for both bats and birds to cohabit peacefully.

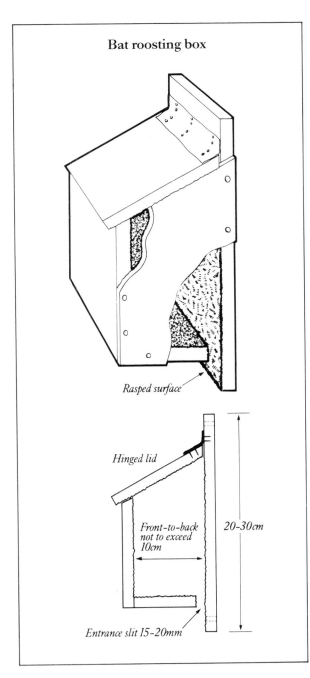

Bat roosting box

Rasped surface

Hinged lid

Front-to-back not to exceed 10cm

20-30cm

Entrance slit 15-20mm

3
RABBITS AND HARES

Lagomorpha

Rabbits and hares, known scientifically as lagomorphs, are more closely related to the ungulates – the hoofed animals – than the rodents which they superficially resemble. Differences in their tooth structure place them in a group, or order of their own (see page 136).

Rabbits

Fossil evidence shows that rabbits were once widespread in Western Europe, but were then forced by the Ice Age to retreat to the Iberian peninsula and North West Africa. It is from these areas that the rabbit has been carried by man and introduced to a whole new range of countries where it has been welcomed as a valuable food source and cursed as a pest ever since.

Pioneering mariners from Spain and Portugal carried rabbits with them, releasing them as future food supplies on the Mediterranean islands they visited. The Romans sent some home from Spain, and the Italians took to them with gusto, keeping them in cages in order to enjoy the embryos and newly born young which were regarded as great delicacies. It is possible that the Romans brought rabbits to Britain, but they were certainly introduced in the twelfth century by the Normans. There are records of rabbits on Scilly in 1176 and on Lundy in 1274, when 2,000 were introduced. In fact islands are ideal for rabbit farming, since there are no foxes or stoats to disrupt the breeding (although the larger gulls operate a measure of control). In the early thirteenth century there was a professional warrener on the Isle of Wight, who provided quantities of winter meat for the Lord of the Manor. The Earl of Pembroke sent ferreters to winter on Skomer Island before 1325 at least, and the rabbits provided a useful source of income.

The medieval nobility regarded the rabbit as an animal of the chase, and kept tight control of the hunting rights. At that time the adult animal was known as a coney, a word derived from its scientific name *cuniculus*, and even now some people refer to its warren as a 'coneygarth'. Only the tender young were called rabbits. As well as the sporting angle, coneys were valued for their meat and fur. They were luxury items. (In the twelfth century the tenant of Lundy was permitted to take only fifty rabbits a year for himself!) Black rabbits were much valued for their fur, which was used for fashionable trimmings, and they were introduced to remote islands to encourage selective breeding.

On the mainland, rabbits were farmed in warrens, and by the fourteenth century the practice was well established, with 1,000 acre enclosures in places as far apart as the Breckland in East Anglia, the Yorkshire moors and Dartmoor (the pillow mounds of Ditsworthy Warren on Dartmoor are still inhabited by rabbits to this day). Inevitably, some of the inmates escaped to freedom and flourished. Rabbits are adaptable, well able to live in a variety of climatic conditions and habitats. They do well all the way from the high moors to the city park and suburban gardens.

Young rabbits fall prey to almost every carnivore and large bird of prey, as well as cats, dogs and men.

Even on sub-antarctic islands they survive the cruel winters by grazing on storm-stranded seaweed.

Landowners have mixed views about them. Foresters and farmers have good reason to dislike them since they devour young crops and trees, yet hunters enjoy the sport and the cash return they offer. Of course, very often the farmer is a sportsman as well, so there is plenty of room for confusion. In law, rabbits are classed as ground game. While alive, they belong to no one, dead they belong to the landowner on whose land they lie. So to take one without permission is poaching.

Rabbits are able to manage perfectly well above ground if they cannot dig (for instance on moorland) but by nature they are burrowing animals which prefer easily worked soil. Sandy hill country with a certain amount of sheltering vegetation, suits them best. Their burrows involve complex tunnellings built on an apparently random basis, with meanders and dead ends. Mostly the system is unlined, the roadways and living chambers are of bare earth. There are many entrances, often betrayed by mounds of spoil dirt, easily distinguished from badger mounds by the liberal scattering of pea-shaped droppings. These droppings come in two forms. The normal, familiar pellets and also a smaller kind,

mucus-covered and rich in vitamins. These are taken as they emerge from their burrows and eaten again, in a fashion reminiscent of cud-chewing in cattle (which are not so distantly related).

A well established warren has been known to have over 2,000 entrances and to provide a home for 400 rabbits, but the average warren is very much smaller. The rabbits range up to 400 metres from the warren, but tend to feed very close to home. If they are undisturbed they will feed openly during the day, but otherwise they are animals of the dusk and night, most active at dawn, especially after a shower of rain.

They graze on grasses, clover and cereals, preferring young plants and very much disliking the sort of long grass which would get their belly fur wet. The closely cropped grasses around the burrow entrances are a sure sign that rabbits are about. Over a period their grazing has a marked effect on the character of the vegetation in the

Rabbits make their warrens close to their feeding grounds. Heathland or pasture suits them best, especially when there are hedgebanks to burrow into. Their close-cropping feeding habits tend to alter the landscape and they cause great damage to pasture, cereal crops and young trees.

Rabbits graze in semicircles, reaching out from one side to the other with their heads, then moving forward to scythe another swathe. But they stop frequently to reach up and look round, keeping a sharp eye and ear for possible trouble. When it comes, they warn others by thumping with their hind feet, then by flashing the white tail-scut as they run. Lacking any conventional defence capability, their survival depends on speedy flight and high breeding success.

vicinity of the warren. They allow dwarf plant forms to thrive, so ground-hugging plants like the dandelion do well. On islands such as Skomer the rabbit burrows are marked by patches of nettle and ragwort, rank species which are not relished by the rabbits and which benefit from the excavated soil enriched with the nitrogen-rich faeces. In fact the close-cropped cliff-top turf which is so springy and pleasant to walk on is kept in this state by the grazing of rabbits. Similarly, the mats of thrift found there are dependent on the existence of the rabbits for if the rabbits are absent, the clifftop grasses shoot up and suppress the cushions of pink flowers.

Insect and bird species also benefit from the rabbits' activities. Ants do well on the open ground produced by their grazing, and so in turn the coastal choughs and green woodpeckers find more to eat.

Rabbits do well on islands, but they also do well in woodland. A young stand of pine is a typical site for a warren, for the rabbits like to be near their food. They nibble the bark of both young pines and emergent broadleaves, which is why foresters go to great lengths to exclude them from new plantations.

Undisturbed, rabbits will relax in the sun, stretching out in the manner of a cat before the sitting-room fire, and they may even sleep out in the open. They have good vision (and may even stand upright to get a better view) but hearing is their most important sense. Alarmed, they dash for the nearest burrow entrance, thumping the ground and displaying their bunny-white tails to warn others. At speed, they may reach nearly 25 mph, and the more usual hopping is a very casual affair by contrast.

Rabbits are gregarious and highly sociable. Their warrens operate in the highly structured atmosphere of a well-observed pecking order. The dominant males keep to their chosen places, the older females are aggressive in defence of theirs; there is continual give-and-take and jockeying for position.

Despite the fact that the rabbit is held up as an example of enthusiasm in matters of sex, the buck chases the doe without apparent relish. When he closes on her they may lie quietly side by side for a while, or they may contemplate each other, nose to nose. The buck will hop around, lifting his tail to show the white flash; he may even leap into the air and spray her with urine, or lick her about the ears. All these activities will be interspersed by short bursts of copulation. Rabbits do not develop a pair bond of any significance and change partners freely.

Most of the does are pregnant during the period January to June and few litters are born outside this season, which offers the best feeding chances for the young. The females become ready for mating early in the year, when the males are already in mating condition. The males then lose condition as the season advances. So it seems that the females control the timing of the beginning of the breeding season whereas the males influence the end of it.

It seems likely that the more dominant females enjoy the safety of the warren to raise their young, while subordinant does have to establish their nurseries at a distance, where they are more vulnerable to discovery by foxes or people. But wherever it is situated the 'stop', as it is called, is an unambitious deadend passage, no more than a metre deep, made comfortable with straw, grasses and moss, with a final lining of belly hair. The entrance is carefully concealed by vegetation. The gestation period is about a month, and though many pregnancies do not result in a litter, the female does not miscarry; she 'resorbs' the embryos back into her system, a process unique to lagomorphs. This behaviour may be a result of high population pressure in the colony or it may occur more frequently in an animal which is low in the pecking order.

The younger does usually have litters of four, but this soon increases to an average of six, in which the sex ratio will favour the females. A few hours after giving birth to the naked, blind and deaf young, the mother comes on heat again and mates. Indeed she may even mate before giving birth and, astonishingly, be carrying two sets of developing embryos at the same time. In either case, while she is raising one litter she is pregnant with the next. And this rapid multiplication is the secret of rabbit success (much the same is true of pigeons, incidentally, birds which enjoy the avian equivalent of the rabbit's sexual reputation). A rabbit may bear anything up to seven litters a year, but on average she will produce twelve young.

This high fertility is matched by the rapid growth rate of the young. Visited once every night by their mother, they suckle and grow. At eight days their coats have grown, they can crawl and their eyes are open. Before they are three weeks old they will be exploring the immediate surroundings and though for a few days their mother will continue to offer milk, they may be abandoned, fully weaned, before they are a month old. The young females will be able to breed less than three months later, and the males will also be fecund. They will continue to be fertile for six years, and may, if they are exceptionally lucky, live to the age of nine.

So why isn't the world crowded, shoulder to shoulder, with rabbits? The answer is because most of them get eaten, or become diseased. Rabbits are a highly desired prey for a whole range of animals, including people. Foxes, stoats and buzzards take uncountable quantities of rabbits, to say nothing of men with guns, dogs, ferrets and even falcons. But disease is a more serious controller of the rabbit populations which are always threatening to explode.

Myxomatosis is the virus which kills rabbits in epidemic numbers; it was deliberately introduced into Britain to reduce their numbers in the late summer of 1953. Within a few years it had destroyed almost the whole of the wild population, leaving only a bare nucleus of stock. Though the virus is passed naturally from one animal to the next by the rabbit-flea *Spilopsyllus cuniculi* (not the mosquito as was first suspected), the disease was encouraged to spread by human agency, because from the farmer's point of view, the extinction of rabbits is a highly desirable goal. But, inevitably, the few rabbits which survived through the chance of natural immunity, set vigorously to their task of breeding, and by the late 1960's there were already distinct signs of recovery. Rabbit numbers rise and fall, but it would be a rash man who predicted their extinction as a breeding species in Britain.

Medieval warreners at work, with ferret and stop-net.

Rabbits are most easily seen at dawn and dusk, though they are active through most of the night. But they are also often abroad during daylight hours in places where they are undisturbed.

Hares

Hares have been fortunate enough to escape the ravages of myxomatosis, though they share the rabbit flea. In behaviour and lifestyle they are very different from their gregarious underground cousin, for they are relatively solitary animals. Their reputation is also a very different one, associated with witchcraft and sinister omens. Perhaps the upright posture and the fiendish scream a hare emits help the stories along. Even today many West Country fishermen refuse to say the name of the creature while at sea, and you should spit on the road and make the sign of the cross if you see one on your path.

There are a whole range of hares inhabiting our planet, but in Britain we enjoy only two – the blue or mountain hare of the Scottish highlands, and the commoner, though vulnerable, brown hare of lowland Britain. The mountain hare is the one which moults to a white pelt or pelage in winter, when it forages under the snow.

The brown hare is the one most of us are likely to see, with its long black-tipped ears and loping gait. Unlike the rabbit, it lives above ground, making a rudimentary burrow called a form. It is a fast mover and has to rely on speed and vigilance for its safety. During the day, it sits tight, motionless and practically invisible. It feeds from sunset through the hours of darkness, and is specially active on moonlit nights.

In the far north the mountain hares moult in autumn to a white coat, but in Scotland the colour is more or less grey. At the southern end of their range, in Ireland, they do not moult at all.

Below: The loping gait of the brown hare.
Far right: Brown hares 'boxing'.

Courtship is a familiar performance, early in the year. The female signals her breeding condition by the scent which is wafted about as she moves her tail, which also acts as a visual stimulus. She 'runs' from the male, flicking her tail from side to side, exciting him with both sight and smell. The jack chases her, growling and posturing. The males chase intruders and jealously guard their mates at this time. If several males are about then there will be even more chasing and displays of boxing. The boxing match, involving much squaring up and use of the powerful fore-paws, may last for as much as a couple of minutes, including a series of chases. But they do not end with the triumphant male copulating with his mate. In fact, the two aspects of hare behaviour which have become part of animal-lore through the centuries – that they go mad in March and that they box for the females' favours – both turn out to have been misunderstood by one and all.

It was my erstwhile colleague at the BBC, Winwood Reade, who made the first observations which led to the dismantling of these myths. She watched hares with persistence, and saw that they actually indulged in chasing and boxing bouts from the January hours of darkness to the light evenings of August. But before March no one noticed because they did it at night, and after

The brown hare has distinctive black tips to its ears. It is active mostly at night. During the day it sits tight in its 'form', completely above ground but superbly camouflaged and practically invisible. When intent on concealment it crouches low and the ears lie flat.

Mountain hares may have completely white winter coat, to match the snow.

March the rapidly growing grass gave them cover. In fact the assumption of March madness being involved with mating should have been exposed as false long ago, since the breeding season was well known to be prolonged, involving several litters.

So the boxing bouts, traditionally and with true chauvinist assumption thought to be an all-male affair of the jacks fighting for the jills, must, she reasoned, have another cause. It transpired that they were, in fact, male-female confrontations where the lady boxed the gentleman's ears because he was being frisky at an unsuitable time.

The gestation period is some thirty days, and there may be several litters of up to eight leverets, though three to four is usual. Each litter will involve a separate, well concealed form being made. Unlike rabbits, the newborn leverets have the full fur coat, their eyes are open and their teeth ready to chew. They need to be ready to face the world, because they are born into it exposed and vulnerable.

Hares are animals of cultivated fields and open country. They are sedentary, feeding on a home range which probably does not exceed a kilometre. As herbivores, they graze on cereals and grasses. They relish clover, and I have watched them in pasture moving quietly from clump to clump, delicately sniffing the plants before picking off the tips. They will also take their share of winter wheat, cabbage and root crops like turnips. Disturbed, they run like the wind, but if they think you haven't seen them they sit tight and motionless until there is real danger that you might step on them. They do not make many sounds, except for the screaming calls of danger or sometimes in courtship. And it is in springtime that it is sometimes possible to call them towards you by imitating the scream.

4
RODENTS
Rodentia

Rodents are characterised by having two large incisor teeth in each jaw. These have a front surface of hard enamel backed by soft dentine and operate as chisels. They grow continuously, so the animal is provided with an ever ready cutting edge which gnaws to devastating effect. This Order contains the largest number of mammal species worldwide, many of them abundant. Some are very large, like the South American capybara, but most are more-or-less mouse or rat sized.

Squirrels

Red squirrels are animals of coniferous forest, though they may inhabit mixed woodland. The flat, sandy country where pines flourish suits them well where they live in the tree tops, seldom venturing to the ground. They are active throughout the day, and do not hibernate, as they are able to feed through the winter because of the plentiful supply of fir cones. Since these take four years to ripen before they fall, the squirrel has a food source which is independent of the seasons, and which is available in the safe upper regions of the trees.

Perched on a precarious branch, the squirrel first gnaws the cone away from its fastening, grasps it with its forepaws and tears off the scales in order to extract the oil-rich seeds. Starting at the base of the cone and working to the top, the job is finished when all that remains is a gnawed stem which has just a few untouched scales at the tip. Beneath a conifer which has been worked by a

red squirrel, the ground will be littered with these discarded scales and cone 'cores'. Unfortunately, squirrels not only take their fair share of the cones, but they also strip the bark from the trees, high up in the tops, in order to eat the soft sappy under layers. The weakened crown of the tree then breaks off in high winds.

In summer the red squirrels will take fruits and berries. They enjoy beech mast, acorns, hazelnuts and are adept at opening the nuts to get at the kernels. When food is abundant, they will cache stores in tree holes and crevices, and even on the ground. It seems likely that they have a general idea where they hoarded their secret stores, but discover the precise spot by smelling their way to it; or they come across it by chance.

If you are lucky enough to live in red squirrel country, you will find that they are readily encouraged to a feeding station for peanuts. I have known three people who have been able to entertain them in their living rooms, the squirrels leaping in through the window to take peanuts from the hand. Brownsea Island, in Poole Harbour, has a thriving population and is a good place to expect a chance of seeing them. Once you have found trees which have plenty of gnawed cones under them, try lying on your back to survey the foliage. The drey is particularly conspicuous in winter. It is a ball-shaped structure of twigs and bark, lined with softer material, usually about 9 metres up the tree and built at a branching point off the main trunk. Don't look for the entrance hole because there isn't one. The animal finds its

Grey squirrels are easily tamed with peanuts.

It is hard to realise that red squirrels were regarded as a serious pest not so very long ago. But they suffered a marked decline in the early twentieth century, when disease killed them in large numbers. This coincided with an upsurge in the numbers of the larger and heavier introduced grey squirrels, but the two phenomena were not related, though it was popularly supposed that the immigrant greys were besting the reds in open warfare. Red squirrel populations have always been subject to large fluctuations. On this occasion the greys just happened to be present and they promptly occupied the vacant ecological niche.

way in by shouldering a way through the loosely fitting twigs.

Because they have an assured supply of winter food, red squirrels can afford to start their breeding season early in the year, which allows experienced mothers to go for a second litter in the summer. So the courtship activity of slow-motion chasing through the canopies, from tree to tree in autumn, may be leading to a December mating, with a first litter born five or six weeks later. The usual number of deaf, blind and naked young is three, but there may be up to six in the litter. Their eyes and ears are operational at five days, they have their first downy coat at about eight days and moult to the first proper pelage ten days later. They are suckled until about seven weeks, perhaps a bit longer, but by eight weeks old the cheek teeth appear and the young are starting to forage. They may even breed at six months, though more usually they will wait till the following year. The male plays no part in the nest activities.

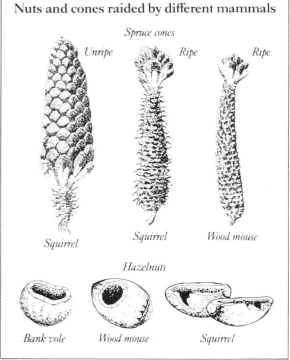

Nuts and cones raided by different mammals

Spruce cones

Unripe   *Ripe*   *Ripe*

Squirrel   *Squirrel*   *Wood mouse*

Hazelnuts

Bank vole   *Wood mouse*   *Squirrel*

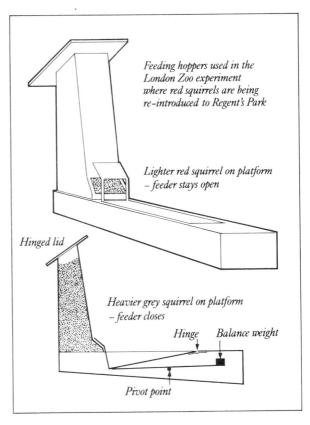

Feeding hoppers used in the
London Zoo experiment
where red squirrels are being
re-introduced to Regent's Park

Lighter red squirrel on platform
– feeder stays open

Hinged lid

Heavier grey squirrel on platform
– feeder closes

Hinge   Balance weight

Pivot point

Scientists at London Zoo are currently engaged on a fascinating experiment in which they have reintroduced ten red squirrels to Regent's Park. Though the well-established grey squirrels show much interest and even chase the reds, there have been no disastrous encounters so far. Indeed, in their turn the reds chase the greys in defence of the hoppers of food which have been provided for them. (These are arranged so that the lighter red squirrels can get at the hazelnuts without difficulty, but the heavier greys involuntarily operate a mechanism which closes the hopper). So it seems that the red squirrels are perfectly able to look after themselves. There is very little likelihood of the two species interbreeding, but there are times of the year when it is not easy to distinguish between them. In winter the grey moults to a distinctly reddish brown coat which can cause confusion, but it never has the ear tufts of the red.

Red squirrels are now very localised in central and southern England (though they are widespread on continental Europe through to Asia), whereas the greys are abundant and widespread. There was a fashion at one time to call the grey squirrel (an unwelcome immigrant from America) the 'tree rat'. This rude name-calling was meant to imply that it was far removed from the more popular red squirrel. It also served to suggest an upgrading of the red away from the rodent clan. But in fact they are closely related, and are both more correctly described as 'tree squirrels' by contrast to the ground squirrels and flying squirrels of other continents.

There is no doubt that the grey squirrel, rashly introduced and allowed to make itself at home in Britain, is unwelcome. But it is here, and here to stay. The extermination programme which was at its height in the wartime years in defence of our tree crops has failed and been abandoned.

Although there were earlier, less authenticated sightings, the earliest firm record of grey squirrel introduction was in 1876, when specimens were released in Cheshire. But then in 1890 the Duke of Bedford released more at the Woburn estate in Hertfordshire. They did well, and regrettably encouraged other people to try elsewhere. The animals are adaptable and a great deal less selective in their feeding habits than the reds, and by the 1960s they had spread to inhabit most of the British Isles. Their preferred habitat is deciduous woodland, but they will manage perfectly well in urban parks and suburban gardens, where they irritate bird-garden enthusiasts by systematically defeating any device intended to provide seeds and nuts for small birds. They will climb along clothes lines to reach a

string of peanuts and they will swarm up any but the most slippery pole to achieve the delights of a bird table. Many people enjoy their antics and their mastery of acrobatics, but they are devastating plunderers of birds' eggs and chicks.

Acorns are their preferred food, so they are happiest in association with oaks, but they also take hazelnuts, cones, fruits, green stuff and the farmer's cereals. In the garden they damage fruit and vegetable crops, in the woodland plantations they feed on newly emergent tree shoots and eat seeds. Most serious of all, they strip bark in their quest for the vitamin-rich inner layers or, sometimes, to release the aggression which accompanies territorial battling. When they ring-bark a tree completely, the tree is killed above the scar. Curiously, in a land where sporting and hunting interests have always been strong, the grey squirrel has never been prized for the table, although in America it is a delicacy. (It seemed to me particularly spineless of the Forestry Commission to cave in to sentimental opposition when they removed grey squirrel from the menu at a recent Tree Conference!)

Like the red squirrel the grey makes a breeding chamber in a drey, although it is rather larger and more untidy, high up in a tree fork. And in making its drey it often uses young shoots and leaves, another activity which antagonises the foresters. The breeding cycle is much like that of the red.

Voles

'Small mammals' are the most difficult to see. Apart from being small they tend to be secretive and nocturnal. Many people would live their whole lives without knowing that they shared their living space and their buildings with small furry four-legged creatures but for the activities of the family cat. Cats make very effective monitors of the small mammal scene. Many a night is enlivened by the arrival of puss proudly bringing a shrew or a vole or a mouse or even a rat into the bedroom. I draw a veil over the prowess of our own family cats which not only bring in mammals but waders from the beach, to our great sadness.

One way to organise an insight into vole life is to lay a piece of corrugated iron in an area of long grass. This offers an ideal retreat for voles to construct their nests in a dry and safe location. Lift the corrugated iron occasionally and with due respect, and you will see the tunnellings and nest-balls. But another device is the mammal table, a variation on the bird table, which has been developed by Michael Clark of the Mammal Society. His station is set up by a window, protected from cats and other predators by chicken wire, and is lit by a lamp which illuminates the night scene with red light. Offering food in this manner (see page 67), he has enticed bank voles during the daytime, and has seen field voles as well as wood mice, yellow-necked and house mice. Clearly there has to be an easy access for the animals, since they can't fly in like the birds. So if you have a window which is close to a hedgebank you have the perfect set up. Otherwise you need to devise a ramp or access of some kind, bearing in mind that voles and mice do not like to be exposed to view.

An interesting thing about the distribution of small mammals is that, while birds colonise islands as if nature provides them for the purpose, small mammals arrive unintentionally, usually carried unawares in a bundle of hay or sheep fodder. In this way, shrews, mice, voles and rats reached islands all round the coast of Britain, and in many cases they settled successfully (to the mixed appreciation of island birds). In the course of time, isolation resulted in distinct forms of these mammals developing. For instance, on Orkney and Guernsey, there is a local version of the field vole, and on Skomer there is a version of the bank vole which breeds at even higher densities than does the mainland race.

Bank voles

Bank voles are abundant on the mainland of Britain, living in deciduous woodland, scrub country, hedges and ditches. They construct a series of surface tunnels and runs, radiating from the nest burrow. Eating green plants, fruits, roots, nuts and fungi, they have a well-marked territory with a home range up to 45 metres in diameter. Unlike the other voles, they are good climbers, and will gnaw bark. They breed from mid-April to December, producing up to four or five litters of young which are weaned in less than three weeks and soon disperse to start up on their own. Small wonder that the species is abundant and represents desirable prey for a whole range of predators from owls to foxes. Its rich, reddish-brown upperparts distinguish it from the field vole, which is greyish or yellowish brown.

Field voles

Like the bank vole, field voles are abundant and widespread, but they are more typically animals of rough pasture. They operate from a series of surface tunnels, and are most active at night but also in daylight. Feeding on green leaves and stems of grasses, they too produce a succession of litters from spring to autumn. Periodically, when the going is good, they breed to 'plague' proportions, and these are the years when owl and kestrel populations soar in response. They

represent an important food supply, not only for owls and kestrels but for buzzards and herons, foxes, stoats and weasels.

Water voles

The water vole is the largest of the voles, and the easiest to see, not only because it is bigger but because it is diurnal and has a well-defined and exposed habitat. Water voles are widespread in Britain, wherever there is slow-running water. Along river banks, drainage ditches and ponds (as long as they have a decent amount of vegetation along the edge and have not been manicured to suit ill-directed civic pride). Even a large garden may offer a home to water voles if, as well as having water, it is suitably untidy. The vole will then pay its way by grazing an area of grass till it produces the characteristic vole 'lawn'. Whatever the habitat, it is this grazed area which will point to the existence of breeding burrows.

Water voles are aggressively territorial, marking their patch with musk from a flank gland, and following regular patrol routes twenty-four hours a day. They feed on grasses and leaves, and also a variety of freshwater molluscs, worms, fish spawn and so on.

The breeding season runs from late March through to September. The nest is situated in a complex tunnel system which has entrances both above and below water, sometimes among willow roots. The female, without help from the male, fells reeds, grips them in her teeth and swims back to the burrow entrance, where she first cuts them into short lengths before weaving them into the nest. If there are no reeds (*Phragmites*) available, then she will use straw or hay.

To see water voles it is only necessary to stand still in a suitable place (almost any pen in a waterfowl sanctuary is ideal!), but they are most active from late May to mid July. Scatter a likely area with some slices of apple and try a watch in early evening. There are places, such as on the Cherwell in Oxford, where water voles will accept offerings of sandwich ends from people in boats.

Lay a sheet of corrugated iron in rough grass and leave it undisturbed. Eventually you may find that voles have taken advantage of the protection to construct runs and nests.

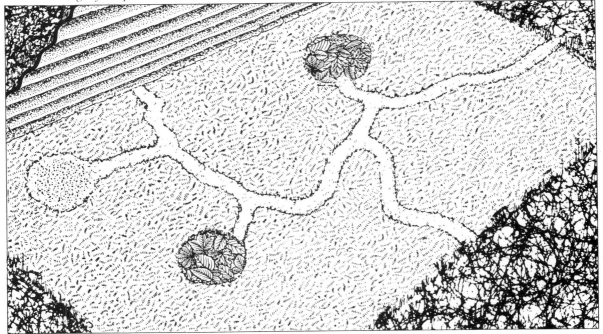

Mice

Shrews have pointed snouts, tiny eyes and small ears; voles have small eyes and ears and short tails; but mice have large eyes, large ears and long tails as well.

Wood mice

The wood mouse, also known as the long-tailed field mouse, is the most numerous mammal in Britain. A woodland species by preference, it is common throughout the mainland, and there are island sub-species on remote places such as St Kilda and the Hebrides. These mice may have been imported by the Norsemen from Scandinavia many centuries ago, or of course they might have come from the mainland in a bundle of hay. Either way, they have ended up as a somewhat larger animal than the mainland version.

For the great majority of us, wood mice are creatures of the dawn and dusk, in hedgerow, woodland, copse, park and garden, places with a certain amount of bushy cover. They have a tendency towards vegetarianism and are seed-eaters by preference, though they also take other green stuff and berries, and a certain amount of insect food in the summer. They can cause chaos in a garden when their fancy turns to bulbs and roots, to say nothing of peas and beans. They store food in their nests, but also in 'secret' places which turn up in odd corners of a potting shed and so on. They will pile food in an old song thrush nest, for instance, or bury it underground in winter. This hoarding behaviour is typical of rodents which are active in the winter, when the store of fruit and nuts provides a welcome energy source. But wood mice keep food supplies in their summer breeding nests too.

The nursery nest is a finely constructed ball of grasses and leaves. It is placed in a chamber at the end of a complex tunnel system which may reach down 60–90 cm beneath the grassy surface, though on occasion it may be in a tussock above

Wood mice (often known as long-tailed field mice) run with tails raised high. They are the commonest mammals in Britain.

ground level. In winter, the mouse is even more likely to be underground, though it may take over the compacted leaf-ball of an abandoned hedgehog nest, or come indoors to the house or a shed. It is quite capable of enlarging a gap in a

door frame and only needs a tiny hole to gain access. Airbricks or drainpipes are other likely entrance places.

House mice

Of the various small mammals, the house mouse is probably the best known to us, and for many people it is the only one they know about. Despite its name it lives outside quite happily if it can find a suitable habitat, for instance a hayrick or a bag of flour in a warehouse. House mice have even been found breeding in a cold store where the temperature was minus 9.4°C. In total darkness, they burrow into the frozen meat, using as nest material the sacking which protects the carcass. In this seemingly impossible situation they have achieved a breeding record of 6.7 litters in a year!

House mice are shy when they are outdoors, but may be enticed to feed at a mammal table.

Urban mice are said to average 5.5 litters, but in a warm and food-rich hayrick they can achieve 10.2 litters, producing 57.3 embryos in a year. The main breeding season is in the summer. In winter the house mice find their way indoors for the warmth, although your house is quite likely to be inhabited by them without your knowledge. If you see a house mouse during the day it is a sign that you are heavily infested. They like to live close to the food supply, so a likely place is behind the fridge, or under the kitchen floorboards. And like the other mice, they can get through an extraordinarily small hole.

House mice are easily trapped using the 'trip-traps' which you can get from hardware stores. But instead of cheese, offer cereal (or nutty chocolate) which they very much prefer. Set the trap against a solid wall, for they always use well-established runs and feel their way along an edge. Cats may take the odd sick animal but are not effective in dealing with an infestation. However, it may be that their very smell and presence will discourage the mice in the first place.

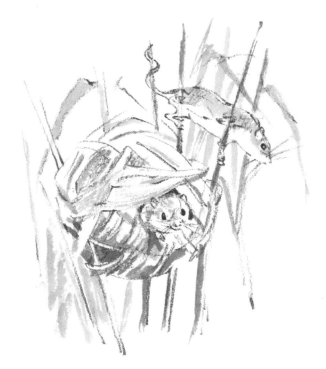

hammock made of living leaves bent down from the stalk. In winter it lives a more conventional mouse life in someone else's underground burrow. Its upper coat is a dark orangey brown, in winter, but in summer it moults to a more russet orange. Populations fluctuate greatly; the most likely time to see them is in autumn.

Harvest mice

Harvest mice are native to our country and are most common in the south and east of Britain. A small and active animal, it has a notably prehensile tail which is used to help it climb corn-stalks and reeds. In summer it lives a high level life in the no man's land between marsh and cereal crop, building a nest-ball of grasses woven into a

Yellow-necked mice

Wood mice are easily enticed to a mammal table if you offer a tray of seeds, but if you live in the south-east of England or in the Severn valley, you may also attract the yellow-necked mouse to the same dish. Larger and more brightly coloured than the wood mouse, they have redder upper parts and whiter under parts, a conspicuous yellow chest patch and a longer tail. And if you live in the country they are even more likely than the wood mouse to come indoors to spend the winter in your garden shed or, better still, apple store.

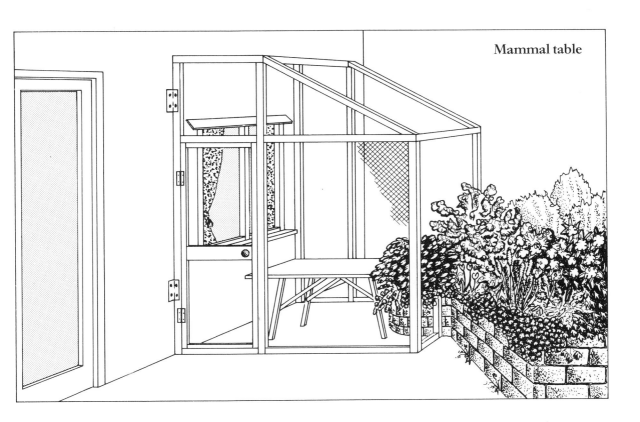

Mammal table

Yellow-necked mouse.

A mammal-table like this is inevitably less aesthetically pleasing than a bird-table, but it may result in enjoyably close encounters with small mammals, which are otherwise notoriously difficult to achieve. Designed by Michael Clark, it is simply a feeding table enclosed with wire netting of not more than one centimetre mesh (thus excluding cats and birds of prey, but not weasels). Offer oats, grass, peanuts and water, and make sure there is plenty of cover in the access area under the base of the frame. If you are lucky you will attract bank voles, field voles, woodmice and even house mice, to say nothing of ferrets and weasels.

Rats

Ship rats (or black, or house rats) arrived in Britain before our now-common common rat, but it is not known how or when they arrived on our shores. Traditionally they are supposed to have been part of the baggage of returning crusaders, and they were certainly established well enough a couple of centuries later to spread the Black Death. Today, they are still associated with seaports and islands. I well remember the days when all ships coming to my father's wharf in Plymouth needed to carry 'de-ratisation' certificates and the warps which secured them to the shoreside bollards had 'chinese hat' devices to discourage bilge rats from deserting.

The common (or brown, field, sewer or Norway) rat reached us from South East Asia by way of Russian ships in the early eighteenth century, and has effectively displaced the ship rat and colonised the whole of the British Isles. It is typically associated with farm buildings, yards, rubbish tips, sewers and rabbit country.

Brown rats (above and right) are abundant wherever there is human habitation. They are successful at exploiting food possibilities – gaining access to the grain in a sack poses no problem.

Relative sizes of some small British mammals.

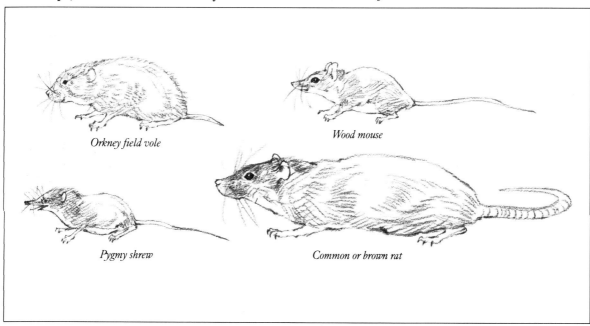

Orkney field vole

Wood mouse

Pygmy shrew

Common or brown rat

In summer it patronises cereal fields, in winter, root crops. And in winter it will enjoy bird-table offerings, climbing poles with agility to carry off one mouthful at a time to be eaten at a safe distance. It prefers cereal foods, but will take insects and even mice, although it seems to live happily enough in close company with house mice.

It is of course a considerable pest, carrying diseases such as *Salmonella*, jaundice and trichinosis, and fouling food supplies with which it comes in contact. In a sympathetic environment such as a warm safe hayrick they will breed through the year, but normally the season peaks in early summer.

Brown rats are normally associated with fouling cereal stores, but they will readily contaminate almost any kind of food.

Dormice

The common dormouse is mainly confined to the south, although even there it is not, a plentiful species, and in the Midlands it is very thinly distributed. It inhabits woodland where there is plenty of dense undergrowth and particularly where there are hazel and sweet chestnut trees. A well-established hazel wood is a likely habitat, especially when it is coppiced in the traditional manner to promote vigorous secondary growth. The dormouse is a secret and nocturnal creature, and the thick undergrowth seems to be a vital feature of its habitat. Devon banks with hedges on top of them are favoured places, and in the old days hedgers often discovered dormouse nests in the course of their work and would carefully lay the hedge around them.

Dormice eat hazelnuts for preference, but blackberries and crab apples are taken, as well as other nuts and seeds and tree shoots and bark. They are arboreal by nature, perfectly at home leaping about the branches. They may be persuaded to feed from bird-hoppers filled with peanuts, and have been heard at dusk rattling the wire to get at the nuts.

The summer breeding nest is made of thin strips of honeysuckle bark, tightly woven, and indeed it may be this damage to your honeysuckle which first leads you to realise that there are dormice about (do not be misled by the more brutal stripping which is carried out by grey squirrels). The nest is often built between the bases of hazel stools in the debris of dead leaves and ivy, or it may be in the middle of an intertwined mass of honeysuckle hanging alongside trees. Often it is 1.5–2 metres off the ground.

Dormice have been known to breed in conventional titboxes in which the entrance hole has been stopped up and a narrow slit provided at the back where the box is fixed to a tree trunk, so that the dormice can climb straight into the box from the trunk. One such box, well hidden in ivy and placed 3 metres above ground, was used as a breeding chamber two years running. It may make

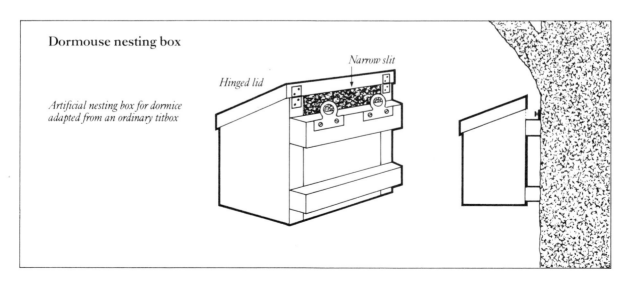

Dormouse nesting box

Artificial nesting box for dormice adapted from an ordinary titbox

Hinged lid

Narrow slit

The common dormouse (not actually at all common in Britain) is an agile climber.

your nestbox even more attractive if you smear mothing sugar on it as a first encouragement to the site.

Dormice are the only British rodents which hibernate, fattening themselves in autumn to roll into a ball and become torpid in a winter nest.

Fat dormice

The fat (or edible, or squirrel-tailed) dormouse is yet another animal which was introduced to Britain by the Romans, who relished it for the table. But the stock which we have at the moment derives from specimens introduced to Tring Park in 1902 by Lord Rothschild. Twice the size of a common dormouse, and looking somewhat like a small squirrel, they are confined to the Chilterns where they survive in modest numbers and can be heard making a persistent and noisy 'churring' sound at dusk in high summer. They have a tendency to invade lofts used as apple stores and have been known to take over bird boxes as breeding chambers.

Coypus

The fat dormouse is a native European, hailing from Spain east to the Caucasus, and from Germany south to Asia Minor. But the coypu, one of the world's largest rodents, is a native of South American rivers and lakes – the 'South American beaver'. Imported to this country in the late twenties and thirties the coypu, or as the fashion trade prefer to call it, 'nutria' (Spanish for otter), was bred in fur farms for its dense and soft pelt. Escapes inevitably occurred and although some of these were in Devon and Hampshire the animal found the most sympathetic habitat in the broadland of East Anglia. A small population of feral coypus had established itself in the Yare Valley by the start of World War II and the Norfolk War Agricultural Executive Committee soon recognised its capacity for damage to farm crops and so set up a sporadic trapping programme. But the fur farms had been established in low-lying districts with slow streams and muddy banks – ideal coypu country, so the animals throve.

Coypus are thoroughly aquatic animals with habits very like those of the beaver. They have dense and soft inner fur under a coarse outer coat. With a long scaly tail for a rudder and webbed hind feet they are well equipped as swimmers and divers, though they are somewhat ungainly ashore. They burrow into the banks of lakes, ponds and slow-flowing rivers and brackish marshland.

Coypus feed on foliage, seeds and the roots of waterplants. They eat the young shoots and rhizomes of the common reed *Phragmites*, often completely clearing reedbeds and creating open stretches of water. In feeding, they choose their plants carefully, taking each species as it comes to its peak, and so enjoying the greatest concentration of nutrients, whether in the rhizomes or shoots or leaves, depending on the time of year. In the case of *Phragmites*, they take the growing leaves in summer, but scrape into the marshy ground for the rhizomes in winter. Their abiding principle is to go for the plant which offers the most concentrated food at a particular time. They will also raid gardens for green vegetables and roots, and farmland for cereals. They are easily attracted to bait, and we successfully filmed them for the BBC TV series *Discovering Animals* by offering carrots and sugar-beet on a raft made out of an old wooden door. Doubtless they would have been keen on apples, too.

The breeding chamber may be at the end of one of the underground tunnels, or, if the banks are not high enough, coypus will construct a platform nest among the reeds, possibly even taking over the nest of a marsh harrier. There may be two litters in a year, born in any season, and the litter will be anything from two to nine young. The female has her teats placed high up on the sides of the body. This arrangement works well, allowing the female to lie in an upright position on her belly, head erect and maintaining an effective watch, with her young arranged down each of her sides. The only disadvantage seems to be that the female is unable to prevent the young from suckling when she has had enough, so she tends to go into the water to avoid them. The teats vary in size and delivery so the young coypus jockey from side to side of the squatting mother in search of the most productive one, forcing weaker siblings to the less fruitful ones, thus establishing an early pecking order in the family.

Coypu society is matriarchal, with the dominant female enjoying the best patch, and the males playing a subordinate role. They are mild enough creatures in reality, but look large and fierce

The lactating coypu has teats placed high on each side of her body. The young may suck while they float, but usually they are fed ashore, and it seems more likely that the teat positioning is useful in that it allows the mother to stay upright and keep a watchful eye open for trouble.

enough to have little to fear from our native predators, though it may be that the occasional juvenile is taken by a fox or stoat. Mink could present a problem to them in the future, but at the moment they are not abundant where coypus are established. They do, however, face the implacable wrath of farmers since they spoil a great deal of the Norfolk reed which is so much in demand for thatching. Also their extensive burrowings introduce the danger of bank erosion and soil subsidence, and on top of all that they damage and eat growing crops.

Early control programmes were not successful, but in 1962 the Ministry of Agriculture, Fisheries and Food launched a serious campaign. Many tens of thousands had been killed through the years without significant effect on their populations, so the first phase of the plan was to limit the spread and contain the coypus within Broadland. In severe winters the females tend to abort their litters and in any case many of the juveniles succumb, with the result that fewer adults are recruited into the breeding population. These are the preconditions which would make it possible for trapping programmes to be effective. In the early 1970's a run of mild winters allowed the coypus to build up their numbers to an estimated population of 20,000, but, after the cold winter of 1975/76, the MAFF trapping programme succeeded in holding numbers back. Increased measures between 1981 and 1984 reduced the population by 60% and the current numbers are estimated at 1,000 breeding females in a total population of 3,000. The target of a ten-year project is total elimination by 1991, but this will involve a heavy investment in research into their biology, which is being carried out by MAFF Coypu Research Laboratory based in Norwich. Coypus are easily trapped and their habitat requirement confines them to a relatively small area. Whereas control has proved impossible in the case of the rabbit, grey squirrel and mink, this might turn out to be a rare example of success.

Coypus are easily attracted to bait.

5
CARNIVORES
Carnivora

Carnivores are predators which feed mainly on other vertebrates. They are active hunters, specialising in pursuit and equipped with tearing teeth.

Foxes

There are twelve species of fox in the world but in Britain the genus is represented by our one familiar animal, sometimes known as the red fox. That name derives from its reddish-brown upperparts, though it sometimes has marked black shoulders, and it almost always has a white tip to its splendid bushy tail. It is the most widely distributed member of the dog family, being found throughout the northern hemisphere, from arctic tundra to African desert. Mountain and marsh, forest and city, all are home to the fox, but for all that it is most typically a woodland animal.

Traditionally the embodiment of cunning and guile, the fox is certainly a versatile performer with a well-developed talent for survival. Foxes are nocturnal animals, but they are very often abroad during the daylight hours, especially before dusk, and sometimes long after dawn, particularly in late summer and autumn. The extent to which they are seen by day depends largely on the amount of human disturbance they suffer. For they are above all secretive animals.

Dr David McDonald at Oxford University cracked some of their secrets when he pioneered the technique of trapping foxes in order to fit them with radio collars. He was then able to track their movements when they were released. He found that on the open Pennines a fox would work a territory of more than 1,000 hectares; on mixed farmland in Oxfordshire a range of 200–300 hectares; and in city suburbs, a figure nearer to 40 hectares. And he deduced that the home range was clearly dependent on the food supply available.

Although the fox is something of a solitary animal, it seems that a small group of individuals, possibly related, may overlap each other's territory so that they meet occasionally. Fox-hunting people will tell you that a near-spent fox will run to another animal which becomes 'it' and, being fresh, leads the hounds away from the tired animal. If this is true it gives the shared-territory arrangement an added advantage.

Away from the city, fox-watching is something of a hit-and-miss activity. Sit quietly in a commanding position overlooking an area where farm or moorland meets the woodland edge and you might be lucky enough to see a hunting fox. They have perfectly good eyesight, but it is their hearing and sense of smell which are their main weapons when tracking prey.

Watch for tell-tale bird activity. When crows swoop down into a likely valley they may be displaying at a fox. Remember that foxes are fond of field voles and rabbits, so try watching the sort of tussocky grassland that abuts a wood. Talk to farmers – they know where the earths are. From a discreet downwind distance watch the earths at dawn and dusk, remembering that the cubs are

The otter's sleek fur is dense and waterproof.

Foxes in courtship play.

most likely to show themselves outside the entrance from April to June. It is in deep winter that you are most likely to hear the blood-curdling shriek of the vixen, just after sunset, and the high-pitched barking of the male.

It may be possible to attract your foxes with bait. Young's (see page 140) make a product called 'Fox Lure' which is said to keep foxes at home when that is desirable for the hunt. But if you live in town, then it is probably a great deal easier to attract foxes than you might think. Almost any food will have them knocking at your door.

Urban foxes are a great deal less wary than their rural cousins, upland foxes being the most unapproachable of them all. (On the other hand, they are likely to be exposed and on open hillsides, so you will get good views through binoculars.) Foxes have been established in urban areas for around fifty years now. Not because they have been driven out of the countryside either by the hounds or landscape changes (there is evidence that foxes are increasing in the countryside), but because they find the city life attractive. Increasing

affluence in the human population has meant that dustbins, compost heaps and refuse dumps offer more worthwhile pickings, and the well-kept lawn offers plenty of earthworms to the fox who is nothing if not an opportunist.

It is likely that foxes first found their way into cities by exploring along railway embankments, which provided biological highways bordered by the sort of brambly scrub which offered shelter. Once they had arrived, they soon discovered bird tables and dustbins. And inevitably, people began to put out food for them. In London, the Wildlife Trust has organised a Foxwatch scheme through which sightings are recorded. It is estimated that the area has a population of some 2,000 foxes; 30% based on public parks, 30% on railways, 20% in woodland and 10% on golfcourses. As yet none have taken to the West End and three quarters of the foxes live south of the Thames. Road accidents account for 60% of recorded fox deaths in urban areas and the average life expectancy for an urban fox is only ten months.

Young fox discouraging fleas.

All foxes enjoy a catholic diet, as biologists found when they examined thousands of fox faeces, teasing them apart to identify prey from traces of hair, bone, feathers and pips. Field voles and earthworms are favourite foods, but they will take most small mammals (they may kill but not eat shrews and moles), ground-nesting birds such as pheasants (which is why gamekeepers don't like them), fruit in season, beetles, even grasses and cereals, carrion and anything off a bird table. They can even get at the rich meat of a hedgehog on occasion, leaving just the skin and spines. Foxes have a reputation as killers, which of course they are, but the implication is often that they kill for the pleasure of it and not because they want to eat. But it is in the nature of the beast to kill if it has an opportunity. If a chicken moves in its sight, it kills it. If, in a henhouse, it is faced by dozens of moving chickens, it kills dozens. In much the same way a marauding fox can cause havoc in a bird colony where there are large numbers of juvenile birds incapable of flight, as, for example, in a black-headed gull or tern colony among the sand dunes.

Fox cubs playing. They are fully weaned before they are two months old.

It is possible to call a fox close to you by simulating the cry of a prey animal, for instance the sound of a hare screaming or the high-pitched whistle of a mouse. Patrick Pinker (see page 140) produces an artificial lure which may serve to attract one. But it should be used sparingly, and at long intervals. If you get it right the fox (or a stoat or weasel for that matter) will hear the call from a good distance, but it will be exceedingly cautious before it reveals itself. These lures are best used in winter when hunting is hard and foxes are least choosy. Dawn and dusk are the best times to try, but don't overdo it, and leave a good five or ten minutes between each burst of calling.

Fox cubs develop their hunting skill in play by, for example, pouncing on imaginary prey.

A fox 'goes to earth' in any number of different situations. He may take over a rabbit burrow or share a badger sett, he may find a cavity under rocks or it may equally be under a toolshed in your back garden. A 'typical' earth, if there is such a thing, will have two or three holes of about a hand-span in diameter leading into well-drained soil. There will be well-trodden paths leading to the holes, which are marked by fan-shaped spoil heaps. If it is in active use you may find footprints in the spoil. There may be flattened vegetation around about, whickering noises from within, and the littered remains of dead prey outside – bones and feathers. There will be no bedding material as you would expect at a badger sett. Put your face well into the hole and take a deep sniff. An occupied fox den will smell acrid, a full-bellied carnivore smell.

The best time to be sure of an occupied den is in the breeding season, for at other times foxes are most often above ground. The earth is re-excavated each year in readiness for the family. But it is very important not to disturb the animals at this time for they are easily scared off and will abandon one den for another. Do not make the mistake of putting food at the entrance – this will spook them for sure.

It is the vixen who chooses the breeding den. Mating occurs early in the year, the dog coupling with the vixen during the period of two or three days when she is on heat. After a gestation period of fifty-two or fifty-three days, the cubs are born in the early spring, a time when there should be ample food. The dog fox plays a full part in bringing food to the den where the cubs are fed underground. By the time they are a month old, they are already exploring above ground, learning to find worms, and to chase and eat the voles which are brought to them in a disabled, easy-to-catch condition. It is at this time of year, in May and June, that you may see the joyful sight of the adults playing vigorous games of leap, jump and tumble with the cubs out in the daylight. This is when the vegetation round the den entrance gets well and truly flattened.

It is a fact that foxes are a great deal easier to see in the south than the north. In the south of England foxes are in close contact with man's works and visit farm, village and suburb with equanimity. In the north this isn't the case. Farmers have a much more aggressive attitude to them and hunt them more persistently. Hunting and killing foxes with terriers, hounds and guns is a major interest in places like the Pennines. As a result, upland foxes are extremely wary animals, keeping their distance from man as much as possible.

It is extremely difficult to judge just how important the fox is as a pest on domestic animals and game birds. There is no doubt that they eat them, but it is very much more doubtful that they do so to a degree that has economic importance. Foxes are accused of taking lambs and chickens and of spreading disease. But with most chickens kept in secure sheds these days attacks are rare. There is no evidence that foxes take live lambs on any scale, though they do scavenge carcasses and eat the afterbirths. It may even be that individual foxes survive entirely on afterbirths for some time during the lambing season. David McDonald spent literally hundreds of hours watching foxes in lambing fields, when they were feeding on afterbirths and also on the tails which dropped off after ringing. He never saw a fox kill a lamb. What's more he has never found any farmer who has actually seen a fox kill a lamb. In fact about the only serious damage that can be laid at the fox's door is the killing of game birds. But this is hardly surprising when you consider that birds like pheasants are stocked at densities which are highly unnatural.

Man is the fox's most effective predator, in terms of hunting and shooting. Foxes are also taken for their pelts nowadays, as they fetch a good price on the continent. But for all that, fox-control as we now practice it is ineffective. The fox is a territorial animal and for each one that is killed another moves in to take its place. Fox hunters have a vested interest in maintaining a good population of foxes and indeed in counties like Lincolnshire with their endless acres of cereal prairie, it is partly to please foxes that the woodland coverts are jealously guarded. Fox hunting is a paradoxical affair in that the primary object is enjoyment of the hunt; success in terms of fox-extinction would be counter-productive. In fact following the hunt may be one of the most practical methods of fox-watching. And whatever the morality of it all, hunting ensures a healthy fox population, and is better by far than poisoning and snaring.

The vixen stays with her cubs all day and much of the night for their first three weeks. After that she stays away during the day.

Pine Martens

The pine marten is an elusive animal. The size of a slim cat with glossy-brown fur marked by a straw-coloured throat patch, gold-rimmed ears and a bushy tail, it is totally absent from most of England and a rarity in the Lake District, Wales, the Scottish Highlands and Ireland.

Pine martens were widespread in Britain till the early eighteenth century, but persecution by gamekeepers both as vermin and because of their fine pelts brought them to near extinction by the 1920s. They are still being trapped, snared and shot, and accused of hen house and gamebird raids, but although they are not a protected species under the Wildlife and Countryside Act 1981, there is a glimmer of hope that landowners and keepers are becoming more tolerant of this remarkably beautiful animal. In Scotland, their main stronghold, pine martens are even increasing in numbers and spreading in distribution. One of the happy consequences of conifer afforestation by the Forestry Commission is that this habitat is sympathetic to the needs of martens. Mixed conifer plantations suit them best, but they also inhabit pine woodland and the sort of scrub that often exists along railway embankments.

They are most difficult animals to see. Hunting mainly at dawn and dusk, nocturnal by nature, they nevertheless spend a good deal of time on the ground, denying the old assumption that they are mainly arboreal. They commonly work along pathways established by men or by deer and badgers, as is evidenced by their droppings, conical piles which are deposited on the ledges of broken cliff faces, rock clefts, hollow trees and so on. They are omnivorous, but small rodents are a prime food source, especially when they are abundant. Mice and voles make up as much as 80% of their diet. They are capable of chasing and catching a red squirrel in full flight among the treetops, leaping from branch to branch and clawing their way around the tree trunks in pursuit. In the summer they will prey on incubating birds and dig honey and bees out of a tree hole. In autumn they will pick strawberries, blackberries and blueberries. In November they will fish salmon out of the mountain burns while they are on their spawning runs, and they will eat carrion. Perhaps most unexpected of all, they are not uncommon visitors to bird tables, being especially attracted to shortbread biscuits.

Pine martens mate in late summer, the male grabbing the female by the scruff of the neck and dragging her about the ground as they growl and purr. Implantation of the fertilised egg is delayed until mid-January, however, so that the young are born in March or April in a den situated in a crevice in rocky woodland or in a tree hole or even an owl nestbox. The one litter a year produces, on average, three young which are weaned in six or seven weeks, though lactation continues for another month or so. They begin to show their faces outside the den in June when they are eight weeks old and develop a wide vocabulary of grunts and growls. By July they will be swarming around trees, but they are not independent till they reach six months old.

In the Scottish Highlands Mr and Mrs Hainsworth regularly attract pine martens to their windowsill with this special fruit cake.

Pine Marten's Cake

9 fl oz (250 ml) cooking oil
6 oz (175 g) demerara sugar
2 teacups stewed apple, including peel
1 lb (450 g) self-raising flour
1 teaspoon bicarbonate of soda
4 oz (110 g) dried fruit

Pre-heat the oven to gas mark 3, 325°F (170°C). Mix together the oil, sugar and stewed apple. Then stir in the flour, bicarbonate soda and dried fruit. Turn the mixture into a large, deep baking tin lined with greaseproof paper, and bake in the oven for 30 minutes. Reduce the temperature to gas mark 2, 300°F (150°C) and bake for another hour.

Weasels and Stoats

Weasels and stoats belong to the genus *Mustela* (see pages 136–7) of which there are three other species found in the wild in Britain: the polecat; its near relation, the ferret; and the mink.

Both the stoat and the weasel have long sinuous bodies and move close to the ground on short legs, with their heads raised. Reddish-brown above, white or yellowy white below, the stoat has a black tip to its tail while the much smaller weasel lacks the black tip to its shorter tail. In the north, the stoat moults to a dense white winter coat, when it is said to be in 'ermine'.

Their habitat is that of the small mammals they prey upon; wet meadows, derelict fields and felled areas in woodland. And if food is available, they will also live on mountain and moorland. They are found throughout Britain, though the weasel is not present in Ireland.

Stoats and weasels are specialist carnivores, concentrating on rodent prey and killing by repeated bites to the back of the neck. Rabbits are an important prey item for stoats, they also take young hares and many birds, and need an abundance of voles and mice. They are active both by day and by night, hunting mainly by scent. Weasels are small enough to hunt through the mouse burrows. They follow a regular hunting route, along hedgerows and fencelines, visiting hayricks and other likely places. They will enter titboxes with great ease in search of eggs or young birds. Both stoats and weasels have a high energy requirement, needing to find meat at frequent intervals. They hunt in spurts with rest periods. A stoat, for instance, must catch an average of two or three voles or mice every day, eating a third of its body weight. If there is an abundance of rodent prey they will kill much more than they need, and store the surplus in a cache.

When food is abundant, litter sizes increase as a consequence. Stoats, which have only one litter, may produce as many as thirteen young, and when the family party is on the warpath this gives rise to talk of stoats 'hunting in packs'. Weasels may produce two litters of seven or eight young of which the first may mature in time to reproduce in their first summer. But rodents are even more fecund when conditions are favourable, so that the changing fortunes of rodents and their predators can be dramatic.

The dens tend to be in hollow trees or rock clitter, under old sheds or in woodpiles or nettle beds, 'scruffy' places of all sorts. Tidier agriculture and 'Keep Britain Tidy' villages offer them fewer breeding options.

Weasels are so small and unobtrusive that you are lucky to see them. Even crossing the road is performed with such liquid grace and speed that the animal will be gone long before you realise what has passed. Stoats, being larger, seem somewhat more tangible. If you have one in view it is possible to attract it towards you, or at least to stop it in its tracks, by sucking air through pursed lips to make a squeaking noise (the sound of a squealing rabbit). Or try 'kissing' the back of your hand to make more-or-less the same squeaking noise. Both stoats and weasels have a lively curiosity and may come to investigate.

Stoats and weasels move with sinuous grace, full of confidence. They pursue their prey through dense vegetation and rocks and even underground.

Both species are regarded as vermin but, as Ian Linn of Exeter University discovered in the course of research, a family of weasels will account for about 2,000 mice or voles in a single year and so play their own useful part in keeping populations of rodents down. Man is their most serious predator, but they are also hunted by owls and buzzards.

The weasel is the smallest of the carnivores. It lacks the black tail tuft of the stoat.

Polecats and Ferrets

Polecats were at one time widespread on the British mainland, but they were heavily trapped for the fur trade and killed as vermin on game-bird estates. By the end of the nineteenth century they were at a very low ebb, restricted to a stronghold in mid-Wales and the Welsh Border country, and just possibly holding on in the Lake District, Devon and Cornwall. But with the gradual change in the attitudes of gamekeepers and greater tolerance of predators, polecats have been allowed to make a slow recovery. They have recolonised almost all of Wales and are working along the Severn Valley.

Polecats seem to prefer the sort of woodland which offers rocky slopes for their dens, but will also inhabit dunes, marshland and riverbanks and co-exist with farmers around the remoter buildings. Their taste in food is fairly catholic, with a preference for small mammals and juvenile rabbits; they will eat frogs and, on occasion, ground-nesting birds. They are poor climbers, and are mainly nocturnal.

It can be a problem to know whether polecats are genuinely wild animals, because they interbreed so freely with gone-wild ferrets. Wild Welsh polecats tend to have a dark chocolate tint, and when they breed with feral ferrets, which are often pure white, the offspring are usually dark chocolate too. This means the progeny may be indistinguishable from pure polecat.

Ferrets are a domesticated version of the weasel family. One theory has it that they were introduced by the Romans or the Normans along with the rabbit, but current thinking is that they derive directly from the European polecat. One of the criteria for acceptance of an animal as a full species is the ability to interbreed freely, producing fertile young, and this is certainly the case with ferrets and polecats. In spite of many assertions to the contrary, ferrets are not believed to cross with stoats and it is even less likely that they would mate with weasels. Ferreters call their coloured ferrets 'polecat-ferrets' and, when they escape to join the wild population, they are easily absorbed.

One of the real puzzles today is to decide to what extent the increasing population of wild polecats is derived from the domestic version.

Polecat . . . but is it pure or crossed with ferret?

'Wild' polecats very often have suspicious areas of white on their coats – usually a throatflash – which betrays a relationship with captive-bred stock. And there is no doubt that large numbers of ferrets go feral every year, after escape or loss.

In domestication, ferrets vary greatly in size, with keen ferreters looking always for small ones which are more likely to be able to slip through the mesh of their rabbit-catching purse-nets. They are actually contented and friendly animals by nature; their undeserved reputation for savagery dates from the days when they were half-starved in the belief that they would be more aggressive hunters in that condition. Ferrets kept in good housing as part of a ferret 'court' are entirely charming and rewarding animals to know – provided you are not a rabbit.

As well as the conventional use of these animals in 'ferreting' out rabbits from their burrows (to be caught in nets by trappers), ferrets have been worked in falconry to flush out prey for hunting birds. Both falcons and hawks have been trained to hunt in this way, but hawks are the most suitable. The ferret is sent into the burrow to encourage the rabbits to go above ground, and the hawk is then released to swoop on the prey. A well trained goshawk, which knows the ferret concerned and has a good understanding of its function, is a highly successful hunter. However, it is necessary to have a licence for this sport which is not at all easy to obtain – to say nothing of the goshawk.

At the other end of the social scale, ferrets are commonly used in docklands to hunt rats.

Mink

Like the coypu, mink were introduced from America, in this case the North rather than the South, by fur farmers. Ranches were first established in 1929, and the first escapees were soon exploring the British scene. But it was not until the industry enjoyed a period of expansion in the 1950s that feral mink began to make a serious mark in Britain. It was in Devon, on the upper River Teign, that the first proven case of breeding became known when a female with young was seen in 1956. Now they are well established, breeding throughout the British Isles, though they are not so common in Ireland. The Ministry of Agriculture has made strenuous efforts to control them but they range widely and seem destined to remain a part of our fauna.

There is a marked difference between the size and colour of feral mink and captive mink. Ranch mink, intensively fed, are twice the weight, averaging 2.5–3 kg. Most ranch mink are mutants derived from the 'Alaska' strain, which is large and fertile, and the 'Quebec' strain which has a superior pelt. The mutations come in beige, blue, and a whole range of browns, greys, whites and black (known as Aleutian, Palomino, Pastel, Pearl, Platinum and Topaz in the trade). They have a dense and soft underfur with long stiff and glossy hairs. The chin is invariably white.

In the wild, mink quickly revert to their natural dark brown with a black tail. They are well adapted to wild Britain, and are not in overly direct competition for their ecological niche. They are agile animals, mostly active at dawn and dusk, though you may see them at anytime. They climb well, but are largely aquatic, being master swimmers with partly webbed toes. They live near water, though they range widely when dispersing as young. The home range may be up to 11 km.

Mink are voracious predators with a wide taste, eating anything that is available, pursuing it by scent. Waterfowl, especially moorhens and coots, poultry and gamebirds (they have been known to take a 2 kg capercaillie) and their eggs, rabbits, small mammals and fish are all on its menu. The dens are in bank holes, tree hollows and crevices, and the nest may be lined with feathers. The single litter usually consists of five or six young which are weaned in little more than eight weeks and are adult in size by four months. They tend to be seen as family parties from June to August, the kits staying with their mother till the following autumn.

Badgers

Badgers are found throughout Europe (except in northern Scandinavia and Iceland), and across Asia to Japan. They are present in every British county but are most common in the south, especially the south west. They are least common in the 'prairie' country of East Anglia and on the uplands. Though they are often abundant they are shy and unobtrusive, keeping themselves to themselves. Many people have badgers living as neighbours they've never met and don't even know exist. They are no trouble and not in competition with us.

Their preferred habitat is deciduous woodland, but nowadays they often make do with the second-best of hedgerow and scrub. They need good ground cover near the sett to be able to emerge unseen. Perhaps this requirement is why the open coniferous woodland doesn't seem to suit.

Badgers are carnivores by definition and dentition, but omnivores by behaviour, eating almost anything. But it seems their first choice is earthworms, for which they mainly use their sense of smell. On a warm and damp night they will 'hoover' a pasture, and one particular badger was found to have 200 large earthworms in its stomach. But they are opportunist feeders, foraging rather than hunting. Given the chance they will take young voles and mice, rabbits and even moles. They will dig for leatherjackets and turn over cow pats in search of beetles. In the hard times of drought they will take gamebird chicks and poultry. In late summer and autumn they turn vegetarian, eating blackberries and windfall fruit, acorns, hazelnuts, cereals, clover, and grass. They enjoy digging out the fat grubs and wasps of a wasps nest, their hair standing on end in the excitement and effectively keeping angry insects away from their skin.

They will collect the hedgehog victims of traffic accidents, cleaning them out and leaving the bare skin inside out. They will patronise picnic places for left-over sandwiches and crisps, and explore dustbins. In fact, badgers will be pleased with food as a gift. Chocolate drops and peanuts are welcome, honey is a sure-fire winner.

Badgers often make easily recognisable scratch marks on trees near the sett.

Badgers are often accused of taking clutches of eggs and sitting pheasants, but this is unusual unless worms are hard to get. They are also much accused of poultry killing, although this is certainly not an everyday activity. More often than not, when it happens, it is the work of an old badger or a desperate act in hard times. The easy solution is to make sure the poultry are housed properly, paying special attention to the trap doors to make sure the badgers can't get their noses into a gap, for they have incredible strength. When I had a badger staying as a temporary guest in my house all doors had to be left open because if they weren't the animal would just get its snout into the draught and rattle the door so noisily that we feared it would splinter.

If it weren't for their habit of digging under rabbit-proof fencing – when it is put up across one of their long-established ancestral paths – foresters would find little fault with badgers. They don't spoil saplings, or indulge in barking, and they eat some rabbits and voles. Unfortunately they will persevere in opening up a hole in wire netting placed across 'their' pathway. The remedy is to provide a swinging gate which is too heavy for a rabbit to push open, and this is widely done around Forestry Commission plantations. After a great deal of experience the foresters have found that the badgers take to them with ease, provided they are properly introduced.

Although the badgers themselves are unobtrusive animals, not easily seen, they leave plenty of evidence of their presence. Scratch marks on trees, tell-tale hairs caught on barbed wire and their well-used pathways all tell part of the story of their comings and goings. During the course of a night they will make small diggings in search of worms and roots and they also make dung-pits in which to deposit their faeces. The droppings are somewhat fox-like, with a long point at one end, but foxes don't use latrine-pits. The latrines are dug at strategic places, near the sett

Coypu look rather like enormous rats but they have blunt noses with widely spaced nostrils. As in the case of beavers, their incisor teeth are faced with orange. They are well designed for freshwater life with webbed hind feet and a dense underfur which keeps them dry even when in the water. First introduced to England for their fur, they escaped from fur-farms to establish themselves in the reed-swamps of East Anglia.

Urban foxes are not the diseased and mangy animals that popular opinion supposes. Dustbin scavenging may not be a delicate way of dining but the result is a well fed fox. Foxes will patronise bird tables and are easily persuaded to visit a feeding station.

By the age of three months these young stoats will be fully capable of killing rabbit and vole prey. The females will be sexually mature even before that time. Litter size depends on the abundance of available food, but there may be as many as a dozen young in the den.

*Polecats were once common in Britain but persecution
by gamekeepers reduced them to a stronghold in Wales,
from which they may now be expanding their range.
The white facial band and ear-margins distinguish
them from mink, but they inter-breed freely with
feral ferrets.*

Badgers are shy and unassuming creatures. They are common and widely distributed but are so discreet in their behaviour that many people have badger setts around them without knowing about it. They have regular feeding patrols and are easily persuaded to visit a feeding station if you provide kitchen scraps or peanuts and raisins. On a long-term basis calf-rearing nuts are probably the most suitable offering.

Otters are notoriously difficult to see. In England,
where they are scarce and very localised, they are
decidedly nocturnal. But around the Scottish islands
and mainland they are relatively abundant and often
diurnal. They are also more marine, and conger eels
are a normal part of their diet, though they will also
eat shorecrabs and even dogfish.

Genuine wild cats are confined to the high woodland and grouse moors of Scotland. They are larger and heavier than the domestic cat, have short tails and are clearly striped tabbies. Unfortunately estimates of their numbers are much confused by the enormous quantities of domestic cats which have gone feral and reverted to the tabby form. The 'wild' cats sighted are actually almost always feral cats.

The buck roe deer seem almost tail-less. Roe emerge from forest cover to feed at dawn and dusk, though they may be out during the day where they are undisturbed. Bucks defend a mating territory throughout the spring and summer, barking at rivals and fraying vegetation to signal ownership. In hard weather they may come to a feeding station for carrots, but they are more likely to come to your garden in spring for the roses.

and also along badger boundaries and main trackways, because they serve an important secondary function as markers.

Dung provides a great deal of information about the dropper and it also communicates information to others. Smells and their interpretation are important subjects in the carnivore curriculum. So dung is to be regarded not only as a waste product, but as an information bulletin (traces of hair, feathers and bones may well be found in a fox dropping, for instance, revealing a lot about its diet). Badgers, like other mammals, use dung to mark their property and territorial boundaries and it is impregnated with a fluid produced by a pair of scent glands which are strategically placed between the anus and the tail. As the faeces pass by they are marked with a rich smelly secretion which produces the badger's musky odour.

The scent not only marks boundary places by way of dung, it is also used by a badger to mark and thus identify other members of its social group. Most members of the Family Mustelidae (see page 137) have a social organisation in which a number of females occupy their own ranges within the much larger territory of a single male. In the case of badgers several adult boars and sows may live together in the same sett, but they may also be dispersed in sub-setts within a common territory. The group may consist of anything up to a dozen animals, so one way and another there is a great deal of chemical communication going on by way of the scent glands.

Badger territories depend on the character of the country and the density of population, but probably cover something like a square kilometre. The most important and the most obvious of their works is the home base – the sett. Badgers are strong and powerful, well designed for underground life with very strong claws on their fore feet. Their tunnellings can be extensive and there may be a large number of entrances. It is not always easy to be sure that an excavation is indeed the work of badgers. Fox earths and even rabbit burrows can have large entrances with spoil heaps outside them. But the badger entrance will certainly be a good hand-span in diameter and there may be literally tons of spoil. There will be latrine pits close by and tree trunks are likely to be well marked by clawing. But the most useful guides to badger occupation are first, the existence of bedding scraps (hay, straw, bracken) in the spoil heap, and second, the absence of the acrid odour of fox. Take a good sniff in the entrance and a badger sett will offer a pleasant, sweet smell. There will also be none of the discarded bones and general food waste that foxes leave about.

Badger setts are almost always on a slope, which makes for good drainage and easy downhill disposal of spoil. They very often face south, and enjoy a certain amount of concealment. There

A badger gate in use.

must be water nearby and, of course, feeding grounds; grass fields rich in earthworms will be preferred. The sett is often established at the interface between two geological strata, where the badgers can dig into soft sand or gravel under the protection of a roof of rock. They certainly prefer to dig in sandy soil.

Underground, there will be an extensive system of tunnels and chambers. One sett which was carefully excavated and surveyed had ninety-four tunnels which added up to a total length of over 310 metres. It was calculated that over many generations the badgers had shifted 25 tonnes of soil out of the twelve entrances. The tunnels did not penetrate far down, all were within 2 metres of the surface.

Badgers do not hibernate, but they are far less active in winter. It is in February that they begin to show themselves more freely at a time when they are courting and beginning the annual spring-clean. This is the time when you may see evidence of fresh digging – new spoil at the entrance. And there will be discarded bedding material which has been turfed out, as well as bedding put out to air. They collect fresh hay into a bundle which is tucked under the chin when the

A sow badger suckling her litter in the underground chamber excavated and photographed by Eric Ashby.

animal shuffles backwards along the path to take it below.

Mating may take place at almost any time between Christmas and October, but the most usual season is between February and May. At dusk the boar and sow emerge for courtship outings in which they chase around the sett area with much grunting and whickering. But at whatever time of year the badgers mate the cubs will be born around February. As in many other mammals, this is a benefit of delayed implantation, a facility which ensures that the young are born at the most favourable time of year. Whereas fertilisation normally leads directly on to birth, in the case of delayed implantation the fertilised egg forms a blastocyst which does not implant itself in the uterine lining when it first enters the uterus. It does not grow either, until the moment of implantation. In the case of badgers, this event occurs around December, so that after two months of foetal development the cubs are born in early spring. This means that the cubs will have time to grow fat enough to face the hardships of their first winter.

There are usually two or three cubs, but litters can be of up to five. The new-born badgers stay below for their first few weeks, cradled in a well-insulated nest of dry bedding. They are suckled for three months, but first begin to show their faces above ground at about two months. By five months they are nearly full-grown. They will remain at the sett of their birth for a year before they disperse, becoming sexually mature in their second year.

It is when the cubs first come out to explore the surroundings of their sett, to play and to learn to forage, that you will enjoy the most rewarding badger-watching. It is an activity to be undertaken with a great deal of care and respect. Consideration for the animals clearly demands that you make every effort not to disturb them, or to deprive them of their learning or feeding time.

Prepare yourself well for the exercise. You will need to be well-covered in non-crackly clothing from head to foot, for dusk is the best time of day for watching and there will be midges and mosquitos (some people use a bee-keeper's hat). Arrive a good half-hour before the light begins to drop away. If you are a new-comer to the sett, start by staying well back for the first few evenings till you have a good idea of the geography and the badgers' activity programme. Stay downwind of the sett. Make sure the breeze is blowing in your face. And be pleased if there is a strong breeze, for it will help to waft your smell away. Make yourself as comfortable as you possibly can, for it can be a lengthy business and you must not move unduly once you have settled. Don't forget the insect repellent! If you can watch from a high seat (see page 117) then that will be the height of luxury, but try to find something to lean back against – a tree or a hedgebank, perhaps. Make sure that there are no crackly sticks or leaves which will assuredly alert the animals once they are out. Make sure that from the badgers' angle you are not in silhouette. And once you are settled, stay still. It is quite amazing how much noise and movement people will make before they realise how acute the badgers' senses are.

Be patient, the badgers must come out sooner or later (they may even be preceded by a fox if they are co-habiting). But remember that they have a number of exits and will choose to avoid you if they know you are there. And when you are lucky enough to enjoy a good evening's watching, with cubs playing and larking about with each other and their parents, do not think of leaving until the badgers are all well out of sight and sound.

It is perfectly possible to acclimatise badgers to the use of torch lights, or even floodlights, but this must be done over a period of time and obviously only at setts which are well protected. Choose one which is associated with a garden or farmhouse, where they are most likely to be used to the smells and sounds of people (although badgers vary greatly in the degree of tolerance which they extend to intruders). Make sure there is a red filter on your torch, for they will be less aware of red light. It is possible to buy special lamping outfits for use with binoculars at night (see page 140). Badgers are only too easily persuaded to eat the food which you may provide for them. Bait a sett with raisins or honey and they will be properly grateful. But do it in good time, so that your scent has dispersed before they come along. They will also greedily devour chocolate drops of all kinds once they discover them, but this must surely be disastrous for their teeth.

Many people feed 'their' badgers regularly in spring and summer, and of course you can lay a trail of food which will eventually entice them to come and feed outside your window while you sit in great comfort to enjoy their visit. When I visited Mrs Foden at Linwood in order to film her badgers, we had six cubs feeding just a few feet from our feet, as we reclined in easy chairs. The light from her room extension gave us first-class views.

Bread is the easiest and most obvious food to provide, and a sympathetic bakery may help you with pies and buns which are still perfectly edible though too old to sell. A suitable bucket of badger food would include stale bread, cakes, sugar puffs (regrettably much enjoyed), stale pork pies, bones (raw not cooked), fat, gristle and peanuts. Tip it out at the badger-table, on the ground where you can see it but within a few feet of the sort of cover which allows them a discreet arrival and departure.

It has to be said that that sort of food cannot really be good as a serious badger diet, and indeed pony nuts or calf-rearing nuts would be much better for them even though they undoubtedly prefer bread. But such food has certainly enabled young badgers to survive in summers of drought when worms are hard to find.

Eric Ashby, who has fed badgers outdoors in connection with his photography, decided to go one better and build a whole badger sett underground in the hope of seeing what normally goes on out of our sight. He designed a sett (see opposite) which provided a filming chamber, a dining room and a sleeping chamber, all connected with the field by a tunnel of drain pipes with 23 cm internal diameter. He primed the way with sausage rolls and calf-rearing nuts, and within one week the first badgers were exploring it (there was a long-established and active sett just 180 metres away). It seems that they are happy to

Eric Ashby (and friend) watching a badger emerge from the artificial sett he has designed. Eric has spent years studying ways in which it is possible to get very close to wild animals without disturbing them.

regard it as a sub-sett and as well as nightly visits for their free meal, when as many as ten individuals have been in the feeding chamber, they import bedding material to the sleeping chamber. Sows have even brought their young cubs to rest in this sleeping chamber, and Eric has been able to get some unique photographs via the viewing windows onto the 'film sett' and feeding room.

Badgers have few animal enemies and one way or another most are killed by man. Many hundreds are killed on the roads every year, when they persist in following traditional tracks

established many years before the roads were built, or cars even thought of. On major roads the solution is to build an underpass, and this has been successful. The badgers are guided to the entrance pipe by a flanking fence of stock wire which reaches out at least 50 metres each side, well entrenched to deter the badgers from digging under it. The underpass is made of standard concrete piping, 600 mm in diameter.

Badgers can be very unwelcome neighbours in gardens when they regard 'your' garden as part of 'their' territory and dig holes all over your lawns to take your leatherjackets. It is possible to discourage them by ringing the lawn with rope which has been soaked in creosote or diesel oil, but be sure to keep the rope in a really smelly condition or they will soon go over it. It may be easiest, and even best, to learn to live with them and put up with their damage. On balance they do more good than harm, living their lives in such a way that they hardly impinge on ours.

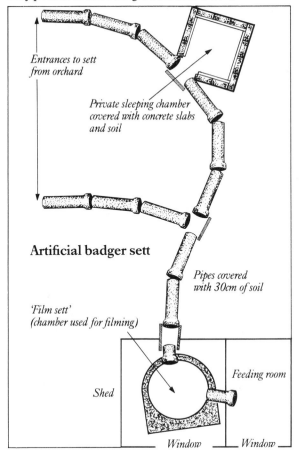

Entrances to sett
from orchard

Private sleeping chamber
covered with concrete slabs
and soil

Artificial badger sett

Pipes covered
with 30cm of soil

'Film sett'
(chamber used for filming)

Shed

Feeding room

Window   Window

The artificial badger sett constructed by Eric Ashby.

Otters

Otters are closely related to badgers but have a very different lifestyle. While badgers are perfectly able to swim, they don't normally indulge, whereas otters are amphibious and entirely at home in and under the water.

Otters are even more unobtrusive and difficult to see than badgers. In Devon they are known to countrymen as 'dim articles' and this refers not to their brains but to their low profile! Most field naturalists will sadly admit that they have seldom seen a wild otter, and then only as a passing shadow or ripple on the water. Nowadays, most otter reports can be more accurately translated as sightings of mink, a common mistake even though otters are much larger and with much more conspicuous tails.

The otter is well adapted to an aquatic life, with dense waterproof fur and a long tapering tail which serves as a rudder. It is able to close its nostrils and ears while underwater.

Otters are mostly nocturnal, probably not by nature but as a response to the continual disturbance of their waterside habitat. It is noteworthy that in Scotland, where there is more room for them to breathe, they are very much more diurnal. Otters are as much at home around the coast and on estuaries as on fresh water, and it is on a tide-washed sandy beach that you are most likely to see their 'seals', the tracks made by the webbed feet as they gallop along in weasel fashion. All their toes are webbed, but there is a prominent heel pad on the hind foot which tends to overprint the forepaws.

It is in Scotland that otters are relatively common on the coast. Their stronghold is the Highlands and islands, where they enjoy a legendary reputation for hardiness. In winter, with temperatures below freezing, they may be found curled up on a wet mass of vegetation, sleeping on a couch which is wide-open to the elements. They avoid the worst effects of winter by migrating to the coast where there is less likely to be ice and food is more plentiful. After a storm, they may well be seen scavenging the beach in full daylight looking for stranded molluscs and assorted animal casualties. A good tip for coastal otter-watching is to keep an eye on gull activity, for a cloud of gulls may whirl around an intruding otter.

South of Scotland, otters are principally animals of rivers, lakes and marshes and they are anything but common, even in southern and central England where they were once widespread. Their food is mainly fish, from salmon to sticklebacks, whatever is to hand. Eels are an important item of diet, since they not only represent high quality flesh, but are easy to catch. If times are hard then

Dog otter swimming.

Great black-backed gulls watch closely in the hope that there might be some fishy remains from an otter meal.

they will take frogs and crustaceans and the occasional vole, while on the beach they will be content with crabs. The diminished supplies of wintertime can be a major problem. Eels will have migrated deep down into the mud or river-bed crevices and shoaling fish will have retreated to the milder conditions of deep water where they are out of the otters' reach. Even voles are less plentiful. But the otters only resort to carrion as a last resort while they wait for the incoming trout and salmon to move up to their spawning beds.

When there is ice on the water they will break through to make fishing holes rather in the manner of polar seals. And, like the seals, they know exactly how to relocate their ice-holes. Even in murky water they are able to fish well, using the sensitive hairs around the muzzle to discover prey by feel. The prey is caught underwater, then carried to an undisturbed place to be eaten. Sometimes you may find the remains of an otter's meal by the waterside. Since they start eating a fish at the head, you will find the tail and perhaps the larger mid-body bones stripped of flesh.

For breeding success, otters need a low level of disturbance, cover for day resting places and secure breeding dens. They are solitary animals by nature, holding a territory which stretches along their chosen waterway and involves a chain of resting places. The dog may patrol a stretch of as much as 15 km whose outer limits might involve a circumference of 35–40 km. Inside this territory there might be one or two bitches ensconced, each with her own clearly defined range. The age and social status of each individual will affect the length and the quality of the riparian rights enjoyed and there will be a certain amount of conflict where a dog otter's territory abuts that of his neighbour. Radio-tracking has shown that an adult dog otter may travel as much as 10 km in one night and that the dominant males enjoy the largest range. Lesser dogs have lesser ranges to go with their inferior status and thus have limited access to bitches, but bitches are less status-conscious and may even breed in close proximity to each other.

The territory is held by force of arms and it is marked, in typical mammal fashion, by scented faeces. In the case of otters these are known as 'spraints' and they are an important vehicle for communication. Otter spraints are deposited in conspicuous places where they will be as clear as a motorway signpost to other otters – on a boulder by the stream, for example, or on top of a fallen tree which is on the waterside otterway. The well-chosen sites are used regularly. A fresh sprint has a sweet, musky smell. It is almost black, shiny and moist with mucus, containing fish bones and scales. The immediate vegetation may be so enriched by this manure that it catches the eye as a lush mound.

Spraints are the most easily found indicators of an otter's presence. Although they have a number of day-time couching places strategically placed at least every couple of kilometres or so along their waterways, these are not obvious and they do not contain anything so conspicuous as a mat of bedding. These hiding places are likely to be in dense bankside vegetation like bramble clumps or hawthorn scrub, reed beds and so on. They might be inside a woodpile or a field drain, amongst exposed tree roots, especially of oak, ash and sycamore, or in the crown of a pollarded willow. The requirements for these day-places are not over-fussy; the animal is simply looking for shelter from disturbance.

For the breeding holt, the otter often goes underground into the riverbank. From the entrance, which may be amongst the exposed roots of a waterside tree, the tunnel extends upwards, at a slight angle, to the nursery chamber which is lined with plant material, reeds, grasses and moss. There will be emergency exits to ground level, which also serve as airways for ventilation.

Otters can breed at any time of year, and do not have the need for delayed implantation. However, there is a peak in late winter and spring. The normal litter is of up to three cubs, which stay together as a family for their first year.

Unfortunately, otters are in decline over most of their range in Northern Europe. Away from the coasts of northern Norway, the Highlands and islands of Scotland and Ireland, where they are still holding their own, they are rare and becoming rarer. In both England and Wales their numbers fell dramatically in the late 1950s and the species was recognised as endangered by the 1970s when it was given full protection in law.

Decline seems to have been due to a combination of factors which are by no means clearly understood. The otters' problems coincided with the time when poisonous cereal dressings and sheep-dips were causing major pollution, and the use of Dieldrin in particular may have affected them, as these persistent pesticides intensified through the food-chain until the animal at the end of the chain, i.e. the otter, received the heaviest dose. The poisons didn't necessarily kill the otters, but had an effect on their rate of reproduction. Agricultural pesticides are now used more responsibly, but even so there are occasional spillages through error or ignorance. Even coastal otters cannot escape pollution, for they face oil spillage, especially in areas like Sullom Voe, in Shetland, where oil terminals are situated.

Otters are not shot or trapped for their fur as was once the case, and they are no longer harried by the hunting fraternity, but a much more insidious threat is loss of habitat. Riverside developments are a problem, and also the over-zealous tidying activities of Water Authorities, whose passion for treeless banks and metalled vehicle tracks is insatiable, as they sweep away any 'obstruction' in the name of flood prevention. To be fair, persistent and well-researched arguments in favour of more enlightened riparian management are beginning to show results, and the Welsh Water Authority, in particular, is making rapid strides towards a healthier, more reproductive and more attractive riverside. There is a move towards reinstatement

Otters live almost entirely on fish – a flatfish in these pictures, but they are not choosy about the species. They tend to take what is most easily available, in spite of what salmon fishermen say! Indeed it is likely that they improve fish stocks by removing the eels which eat trout spawn. They are active hunters, searching in mud and under stones. They catch prey in their mouths and use their forepaws to handle it, if necessary.

If fish are plentiful the otter may kill large numbers, but take only a few mouthfuls in a somewhat wasteful manner. Apart from fish they will also eat frogs, birds and small mammals.

The otter's undercoat is dense and waterproof, so that the animal is dry in the water. Its feet are webbed, and it can travel fast underwater, staying down as long as four minutes.

of otter-worthy habitat, and this more sympathetic management turns out to be in everyone's interest, including that of the accountants. River engineering is moving to a new phase where the requirements of water and flood control can be carried out in the context of a landscape which still tolerates trees, edge scrub and the delightful profusion of colourful water plants.

The continual disturbance of the waterside by fishermen, boaters and various groups of people in search of recreation (and otters) is certainly a factor in the otter decline, so it is important that we who cause the problem should make some effort towards solving it. Since it has become clear that otters are heavily dependent on suitable habitat for resting and breeding places, there has been positive action in favour of improving this. The Vincent Wildlife Trust (address on page 140) is doing sterling work in researching otter needs and establishing otter 'havens' in collaboration with waterside landowners. Their general aims are to achieve minimum human disturbance, improve bankside vegetation by tree and scrub planting and the provision of artificial day-couches and dens. Of course, sufficient natural food is of prime

importance, but uninterrupted waterside cover and suitable breeding places are the next consideration. It may be sufficient to introduce a stable pile of masonry, rubble or logs, which have at least two tunnels leading into one or more cavities roughly a cubic metre in size. The entrances may be above or below water, but ventilation is important. The breeding holt is then covered with turf or sticks, leaves and general debris to make it waterproof and to make it look as inconspicuous as possible. Obviously the artificial holt should be by the water, but above flood level and far away from footpaths as possible.

Provided there is plenty of cover, otters are perfectly able to co-exist with people. They have been seen slipping past dozy fishermen without anyone being any the worse off. They may have a passing brawl with domestic dogs but this usually comes to nothing. It has been suggested that otters suffer from the increase in the population of feral mink. Certainly they share a common interest in prey and the number of mink has increased as dramatically as the otters have declined, but it seems most likely that the plight of the otter is to be laid firmly at our own door.

Wild Cats

Unlike the otter, the very rare wild cat is increasing. After many generations of persecution by grouse-moor gamekeepers, attitudes are slowly changing to greater tolerance of competing predators. But for all that, your chance of a glimpse of the large wild tabby with the blunt tail is slim indeed. You must repair to the Scottish Highlands and concentrate on the edge country between the high forest and open moor. The wild cat is nocturnal, but is active at dusk and dawn, hunting for rabbits and hares, and also mice, voles and birds.

It is in autumn, when they are building up winter fat reserves and hunting most seriously that you are most likely to catch a glimpse. But then there is the serious problem of identification, since there are plenty of gone-wild domestic cats at large, and these quickly revert to the ancestral tabby colouring of the wild cat. In fact, it has to be said that you are most likely to see one in a zoo.

The wild cat is distinctly larger and heavier than the domestic cat; it is always striped and has a shorter, bushier tail with a blunt black tip. In Britain its range had been reduced by persecution so that by the 1870s it was restricted to the Scottish Highlands. It has slowly spread south since the First World War, however, and has now reached to the Borders.

6
DEER

Cervidae

There are two families of ruminants, one (cattle, goats, sheep) is characterised by the possession of horns, the other (deer) by antlers. Deer are herbivores – browsers and grazers. They have a complex four-stage stomach in which the first is a store where food is held pending mastication, otherwise known as 'chewing the cud'. In the second chamber micro-organisms begin to break down the cud, but it is regurgitated yet again for an extra chewing. The food then goes through the third, but it is not till it reaches the final chamber that acid digestion takes place.

Red Deer

Red deer are the largest wild land animals in Britain. They are most abundant in the high grass and moorland of the Scottish Highlands and islands, but are also found in the Lake District, Exmoor, the Quantocks and parts of Ireland. There are also some small herds in the southwest and parts of the south and east of England which are the result of parkland escapes. For all the 'Monarch of the Glen' image, they are by preference animals of the forest and forest edge. They exist as poor specimens on moorland, when they are driven there by the destruction of forests. Nevertheless, they are perfectly capable of living in a wide range of habitats from above the tree line on mountains to low-lying grassland.

Deer enjoy a well-developed social structure which is dominated by the older females in a classic matriarchy. Most of the year the sexes are segregated, occupying their own territories. In the Highland winter the older stags graze lower slopes while the hinds are high up the glens with the yearling calves. Then in summer the positions are reversed with stags occupying commanding positions while the hinds and young graze below. But in the more favourable woodland situations the stags occupy the edge country while the hinds are inside.

Red deer are most active at dusk and dawn. Provided they are not disturbed, they are not particularly nocturnal. During the day they will rest, then feed and drink as the light begins to fade. They will eat almost anything that is vegetable. Grasses, sedges and rushes are the preferred foods, but heathers, leaves, bark and the young shoots of trees are also taken. It is hard work for even a sturdy tree like the Scots pine to establish itself on open moorland if there are deer about. Red deer will turn to farm crops if food is scarce, and have even been known to visit bird tables in a hard winter.

It is only the stag which has the magnificent antlers (the occasional antlerless stag is known as a hummel). Cattle and sheep have permanent horns which consist of a horny sheath on a core of bone, but deer antlers are formed of solid bone which is shed every year in early spring. The older and more mature stags cast earliest, yearlings later in the year. After casting, the stag will gnaw the discarded antlers in order to absorb minerals which will aid the formation of new ones. These begin to grow at once, reaching full size by the end

In Richmond Park the deer lead genuinely wild lives, yet it is possible to observe them closely with ease.

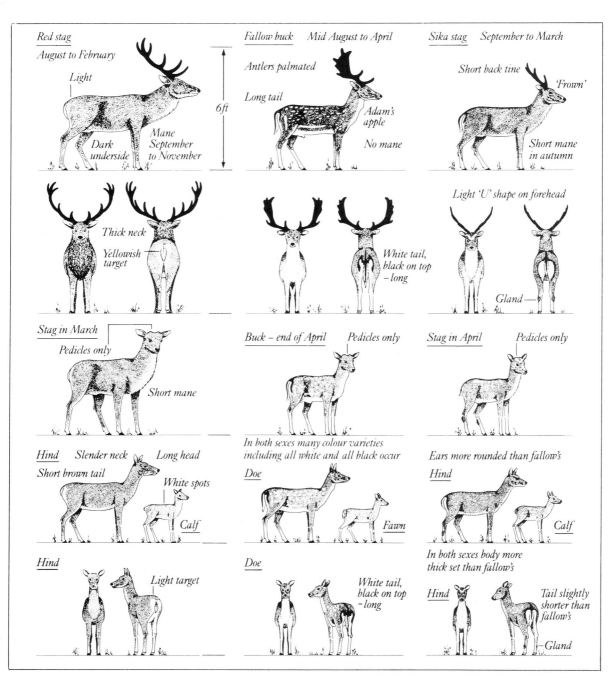

Red stag
August to February
Light
6 ft
Dark underside
Mane September to November

Fallow buck   Mid August to April
Antlers palmated
Long tail
Adam's apple
No mane

Sika stag   September to March
Short back tine
'Frown'
Short mane in autumn

Thick neck
Yellowish target

White tail, black on top – long

Light 'U' shape on forehead
Gland

Stag in March
Pedicles only
Short mane

Buck – end of April   Pedicles only

Stag in April   Pedicles only

Hind   Slender neck   Long head
Short brown tail
White spots
Calf

In both sexes many colour varieties including all white and all black occur
Doe
Fawn

Ears more rounded than fallow's
Hind
Calf

Hind
Light target

Doe
White tail, black on top – long

In both sexes body more thick set than fallow's
Hind
Tail slightly shorter than fallow's
Gland

of July. Then in August the protective covering of 'velvet' (furry skin which covers the growing antlers) is cleaned off. At this point the sex organs mature and the stag prepares for the rut.

During the rut the stag's neck thickens and he develops a mane of hair while his winter coat comes into its prime. He wallows in a peaty puddle which makes him look black and fearsome. His larynx develops to provide him with a mighty voice for 'roaring'. At other times of the year the stag is mainly silent. But in the courting season he roars incessantly, by day and even more by night, having moved in to the hind's territory – the only time of the year when the mature sexes are together.

The rutting territory may occupy up to a dozen hectares and it is marked mainly by the sound of roaring but also physically by the spraying of urine and scent-marking from a hind-foot gland. The stag also deposits scent on the frayed branches of trees when he cleans the velvet off his antlers at the beginning of the rut, and he can flip tears from his eyes to sprinkle leaves. In fact he has a whole armoury of scent glands to make sure his presence is 'well smelled'.

The stag rounds up as many hinds as he can manage, anything up to fifty, and bellows his success to all rivals. By the end of the rut he has lost a lot of weight and his condition is less than perfect.

The pregnant hind has a gestation period of eight months before the single calf is born in mid-summer, usually in June. It lies doggo for the first few days, well hidden in the bracken, only standing to be suckled when the mother visits.

During the rut, stags wallow and blacken themselves in pools of muddy peat.

After a week or so it will begin to follow the hind, especially in the evening, until it joins the herd at a month old. But it continues to be suckled for the best part of a year, even longer if the mother does not become pregnant again.

The female calf will be fertile in her third year, but the male, although he may well be fecund even at one year, will have precious little chance of performing in face of strong competition from older animals. In fact the newborn calf is much more likely to die in its first year than to mate. The average life span though, is probably five or six years with a possible maximum of around twenty.

The stag's antlers improve in both size and complexity till he is six years old; thereafter they may slowly decline in splendour. In the language of the hunt, a stag is called by a series of names according to his age: in his first year he is a calf, then a knobber, a brocket and a staggard till in his fifth year he becomes a hart. A hart with twelve 'points' to his antlers is a royal. And in the old days, when a royal was reserved for the sport of a king, if the monarch failed to kill it the escaping stag became a Royal Hart Proclaimed, and a heavy fine awaited anyone who killed it. Sixteen points is the most a stag can hope to achieve in the wild,

and indeed the average is eight. And the less sheltered the life the smaller and less impressive the antlers. A well-pampered park stag from the soft south will be heavier and carry far more impressive antlers than any monarch of the Scottish glens.

While the stag in rut is an awesome sight, and this is no time to approach it closely, the red deer's main defence mechanism is a quick getaway. But before breaking into a retreating gallop it will bounce a few times in a curious series of stiff-legged jumps, presumably to send a warning signal to others.

A few new-born calves may be taken by foxes or even by golden eagles, but by far the most serious predator on deer is man and his activities. Many are killed by traffic on roads, many are poached, some are shot by hunting (stalking in Scotland), most die of starvation.

The field naturalist will use the techniques of the hunter in order to observe his quarry and to learn more of its ways. And in the case of deer he is tracking a noble beast and following the sport of Kings. The hunt was once regarded as a training ground for warfare. The naturalist's mammal-tracking should be a step on the way to more enlightened management in the form of conservation.

There are some simple rules for stalking, which apply whether your quarry is deer or badger. First of all, wear clothes which suit the season, but make sure the outer coating is drab. Your anorak should be of a fairly boring olive green or brown mix, and most importantly your clothes should not rustle, crackle and pop. Sportsmen and birdwatchers alike tend to go for something like the famous Barbour jacket because it has been successfully developed after a lot of practical field use. These jackets have pockets in the right places and hoods which fold back easily and they are weatherproof without being subject to an excess of condensation. Deerstalker hats are actually useful in the field, since they break up the head silhouette and give some camouflage as well as discouraging midges from getting at your scalp. Rubber soled boots are vital. Baggy pants may not be fashionable but again they help to break up your outline. Dark green woolly mittens serve to cover the paleness of your hands.

Move slowly upwind to your target area, in early morning or evening. Move like a stalking cat, stopping often to look round slowly. Use your binoculars. Try not to crack sticks, but don't worry too much if you do, because plenty of animals crack sticks in the course of their movements. Be still and quiet. And when you do see your deer, stay still and quiet, and don't move in on them for it is a certainty that you will disturb them and they will be off.

At rutting time, in autumn, when the stags are 'belling', you may want to try your hand at blowing a 'stag roarer' (see page 140). This device produces a fearsome bellow if you have powerful lungs. The object is to convince the stag in residence that you represent a potential rival in which case he will come closer and exchange insults.

Deer stalking is still a sport associated with social status, its origins go back to William the Conqueror and a string of monarchs who enjoyed the chase. From mediaeval times much of Britain was reserved as royal forest for the prime use of the King and his privileged guests. Vast acreages were enclosed as deer parks so that landowners could enjoy exclusive hunting, and though their popularity has waxed and waned, they are with us even today, though in much reduced numbers. Richmond Park in London is perhaps the most famous example and it is an excellent place to see deer in a near-natural setting.

In more open country, it may well be that the red deer are only tolerated by farmers and landowners because they enjoy hunting them. This is almost certainly true of Exmoor, where if it

| First | Second | Third | Fourth | Fifth |

Antler development in a roe buck.

weren't for the existence of the Devon and Somerset Staghounds there would be no deer in this area. They can cause havoc to farm crops and would be shot to extinction if it were not for the fact that farmers enjoy the hunt for both the exercise and the social encounters. So you have the central paradox which is so puzzling for the more sentimental opponents of hunting – that the deer are preserved by those who have most reason to exterminate them. They are hunted by those who want to see them survive. Hunting people often say that hunting is the only effective way of controlling the deer population, but in fact this is not true. When serious culling is necessary it is invariably carried out by driving and shooting.

More recently, the farmers and foresters who have most reason to resent the depredations of deer on their crops, have taken the logical course of farming the deer, since venison is high quality meat and the market for it is growing. On the island of Rhum, in the inner Hebrides, the Nature Conservancy is conducting research into the biology and management of deer on what is effectively an enclosed deer park, albeit an island 'enclosed' by water which effectively stops the deer from escaping. The object on Rhum, where the native stock was exterminated by man towards the end of the eighteenth century, is to maintain a healthy population which is harvested to maintain a balance of age groups rather than to achieve trophy 'heads'.

In fact the best heads are to be found in park deer in the south of England and the herd in Warnham Park is a good example. The management is devoted to producing bigger and better animals. One beast to the acre is the rule and they have the best of pasture. Haphazard breeding is not encouraged and the general rule is three to four hinds to a stag. All is strictly managed, and the results speak for themselves.

Sika

Sika deer are related to red deer, but are not native to Britain. Whereas the red deer's distribution covers much of the Palearctic and North America, sika originate from Asia and Japan. They have been introduced to New Zealand and the USA as well as Europe. The first arrivals in Britain were presented to London Zoo in 1860. Other parks soon possessed specimens and in due course some of them jumped the fence. There are now feral herds living in Dorset, where they are well established, in Hampshire and Yorkshire, as well as several counties in Scotland and on the island of Lundy in the Bristol Channel.

Sika are at home in deciduous or mixed woodland as long as there is plenty of cover in the undergrowth. They are most active at dusk and dawn, when they come out to graze pastureland. They browse trees and are particularly fond of hazel shoots. In autumn they will take sweet chestnuts and acorns. Their behaviour and life cycle is similar to that of the red deer. And although they are not quite as large as the red deer, they hybridise, thus paving the way for confusion in the future. They are pugnacious creatures, inclined to stand and engage in browbeating with a human intruder rather than resorting to the more typical deer reaction of instant flight.

Sika deer at the woodland edge enjoying the shelter of a reed bed on Brownsea Island in Poole Harbour, Dorset.

Fallow

Fallow deer are natives of Southern Europe and Asia Minor, though they lived in Britain during the last interglacial period. They were reintroduced to Britain, probably by the Normans. They were highly regarded both for their meat and for the hunting sport they offered and as the years went by many enclosures – deer parks – were constructed to provide exclusive and easy hunting for landowners. By the early seventeenth century every English gentleman of standing had a substantial acreage of park surrounded by a high wall or a ha-ha which was designed to keep the deer within bounds. The Civil War upset the status quo, and since then other wars and hard times have seen the number of secure deer parks much reduced, but there are still fine examples to be seen, as at Petworth in Sussex. And if you visit Charlecote Park in Warwickshire you may still see a fine herd of fallow fording the Avon as they move from one feeding ground to another in a most attractive daily migration.

Fallow deer display an impressive range of variations in their coats, varying from nearly white to nearly black by way of chestnuts, fawns and greys, spotted and dappled. The variety known as Menil retains its spots during the winter.

In law, ownership of park deer has always depended on their being inside the fence. If they wandered outside, they then belonged to the person whose land they trod (and any damage they caused was his problem). Inevitably, through the years, either by luck or exceptional skill or because

A fallow buck disturbed and running for cover. Over a period of time it is possible to encourage fallow to a feeding station despite their innate wariness.

the walls had been breached, deer found their way out of the enclosures. So a well-conducted park not only kept its fences in good repair but provided a one-way ramp which allowed deer from outside to find their way inside with ease. These 'deer-leaps' may still be seen at many parks, with their ramp leading gently up to the top of the wall. From inside the park, of course, they present an unjumpable vertical wall.

However, many of the escapees preferred their freedom and they often found a sympathetic landscape on the wild side of the wall. Fallow live comfortably in the sort of woodland, arable and pasture that was the pattern of British agriculture in the seventeenth century and, indeed, they still survive as feral herds in large numbers. In places like Epping Forest, Cannock Chase and the New Forest, there are long-established herds. Fallow are present in most of the countries of the British Isles, though they are perhaps less well distributed in Scotland. They do well even in close proximity to towns and cities, though they suffer hugely from incompetent poaching and the air rifle brigade.

Fallow are at their most wary during the day, as most deer are, and show themselves mostly at dawn and dusk. With care and sensitivity, it is possible to encourage a rutting stag to display to you in late October or November, and the 'stag roarer' (page 140) may just possibly do the trick for you, reproducing the appropriate grunts and groans of the incumbent buck. But you are much more likely to see your quarry bound off in dismay, 'pronking' in a stiff-legged gait as it warns the others by jumping on all four feet, so don't bother them unduly.

It is not difficult to encourage fallow to a feeding station, however. They may well come to your garden to enjoy your fruit, or you may prefer to offer pony or calf-rearing nuts, or maize tails – all will be gratefully received. Keep well out of sight, sound and smell at first, only revealing yourself over a period of weeks, but in the end you could be handfeeding. Of course the easiest way of all is to go to a well-established feeding-place such as Boldrewood in the New Forest, where the Forestry Commission provide an excellent introduction to wild deer with high seats, observation hide and all. There, you will have little difficulty in persuading a splendid fallow buck to take a potato or cattle nuts from your hand. Early August is probably the best time. In spring they are preoccupied with antler-casting and in autumn they are even more preoccupied with the rut.

'High seats' were developed by the Forestry Commission originally as shooting platforms. They make excellent viewing places for watching deer.

Roe

The rise of the Forestry Commission and its zeal for conifer afforestation has decidedly benefited the population of roe deer, which have increased in unison with the trees. At the end of the nineteenth century some four per cent of Britain was forested; now the figure is more like ten per cent. The increase is largely in conifers which are more easily tolerated by roe than the other deer. However, the stage reached by the growing trees is significant for the deer, and the species of conifer may influence the density of roe populations. Roe are most abundant in a plantation where the trees are in their fifth year. Before this they lack cover and after it the canopy begins to close and there is not so much ground-level food on offer.

Roe deer are found almost everywhere in the south and the north, but not in the Midlands or Wales. Woodland is the crucial feature of their habitat and scrubby woodland, not too wet, suits them best. They need cover in which to hide, so young woods are best; older ones have no underlayer providing both cover and food. The New Forest, for instance, is typical of the kind of country which does not suit roe well, and there are very few there.

They are also found along field headlands and even colonise suburban areas provided always that there is plenty of cover. But it is most difficult to make an informed estimate of their numbers as they are so dispersed. They can be a pest, especially to foresters, by eating young shoots and fraying and barking trees, but the problem depends to a certain extent on the tree species and even on the part of the country. In Surrey, where there is an abundance of food, Norway spruce is not attacked, whereas in Scotland the young spruce will be destroyed. In Surrey the Forestry Commission reckon there may be anything from

Roe deer have an unfortunate liking for roses in a well kept garden. They also enjoy strawberries and browse the leaves and buds off apple trees.

forty to sixty roe in 100 hectares of deciduous woodland, whereas in Scottish pine forest there will be fewer than twenty. The better feeding in the south is also reflected, as in red deer, in the increased size and general condition of the animals.

Roe deer are capable of astonishing increases in numbers if conditions are favourable. An unchecked population may increase by as much as forty per cent in one year, even taking account of natural losses. Not so long ago they were regarded as vermin, to be shot, snared, driven by dogs and taken by any means. Now, in more enlightened times, we only shoot them, but they are adept at evading the hunter, and, accordingly, are equally difficult for the field naturalist to get to grips with. Red deer and fallow they can be seen easily in parks such as Richmond in conditions which are as near natural as could be reasonably wished. But roe have never been a suitable species for parks. They have always lacked the social status of the larger, more extrovert, reds and fallow. They are more solitary creatures, and thus not suitable for the high-density numbers which made for good sport (kept at artificially high levels they develop stress problems). And they graze rather adventurously whereas the others act as useful grass mowers, providing a well-manicured landscape. One way and another, the roe is something of a peasant compared with the highly regarded and larger fallow and red deer. To see them, you must venture into the wild.

Unlike the other deer, roe do not live in family groups (though books will often tell you that they do). The bucks are largely solitary. The largest unit will be a doe with her twin fawns, for the sexes live separately, with overlapping ranges to provide for meeting when the time is ripe. Winter is the only time when roe deer may congregate at a well-provided feeding place and when the older bucks will tolerate young ones.

The best time for roe stalking is an early

Roe deer are most abundant in newly established conifer plantations, but you are most likely to see them in areas where human disturbance is slight.

morning in April, for a number of reasons. In winter they are less active, but as their appetite increases in spring, they must explore to find food at a time when it is in short supply. And in spring the older bucks no longer tolerate the young, forcing them to disperse to try to find territories of their own. And after the winter frosts and snow, cover is least effective, giving you more chance of seeing the animals.

You stand the best chance of seeing roe in places where human disturbance is minimal. Here they will be less wary and more inclined to be out in daylight. Young conifer plantations mixed with thicket and clear-felled areas are a good bet, also mature beech woods with open clearings. By far the best time of day to stalk is early morning.

Move very slowly. Very slowly indeed. Stop every 30 or 40 metres to scan through your binoculars. You are not looking for a whole deer but for a give-away part of it – a leg or an ear or a white rump patch. Watch for movement, anything that catches your eye. And bear in mind that it is highly likely that the deer will hear you long before you see it.

Deer use their hearing most of all in avoiding detection; smell and sight are of secondary importance. In fact roe have poor sight – it is even possible to stalk one across a field while you are in full view, but you need to be good at it. Stay downwind, move fast when its head is down, freeze when it looks up. And don't be misled by those pictures of Scotsmen crawling on their bellies across the heather moorland; in woodland you won't see a thing if you follow their example. Keep a sharp eye open for fresh hoofmarks – 'slots' – in wet mud. And in spring look for signs of fraying and scraping on trees as indicators of their presence.

At the end of May the older pregnant does will push their yearlings out into the world, but this dispersal does not offer as many viewing opportunities as the movement of bucks in April. And after May, the rutting time of July and August offers the best watching. This is a time when, if you are lucky, the roe are so engrossed that they are inattentive.

If you can make friends with the foresters, you may get the chance of watching from a 'high seat', and this is probably the most effective and enjoyable technique. The seat will have been carefully sited over a likely place, perhaps a well-used patch or a feeding area in a clearing or a forest ride or a young plantation. Don't get to it in pitch dark, for you are bound to make extra noise, and it is important to stick to the path which will have been cut to reach it. Remember there may already be deer about as you arrive, so be quiet. And in due course leave as quietly as you came.

The roe rut takes place in July and August, initiated by the doe who attracts the buck to a carefully chosen place on his territory. He chases her round and round in a circle or a figure-of-eight which becomes so well trodden that the excited animals are 'in a rut', from which the mating-time takes its name. But these rings are not at all easy to find, taking up surprisingly little space and in dense thickets, often with a natural hummock or a bush at the centre. To make things even more difficult the deer do not even use the same ring every year.

At rutting time it is possible to attract the bucks by using a squeaky whistle which imitates the call of the doe. These whistles are produced commercially (see page 140) but you could try taking the squeak out of your teddy bear, it has been known to work. Certainly rutting time is when you are most likely to attract a hopeful buck who may come really close. Whether this is a particularly kindly thing to do or not you must decide for yourself.

There are other ways of bringing roe deer close for observation. They will be grateful for a salt lick, for example, which provides welcome minerals. You may have some success with carrots too and these are certainly worth trying, but even these will only work if conditions are severe, with snow covering their natural food. In Germany, where they endure even worse winters than ours, roe are attracted to haybags slung from trees. They can be a real problem in an orchard where they browse the leaves and buds off apple trees, and may even eat the whole tree when it is young. But they are most likely to find their own way into your garden to enjoy your roses, strawberries and ornamental shrubs. Brambles are part of their staple diet, and – unfortunately for gardeners – roses and strawberries are related to blackberries! So create natural woodland conditions in your garden and you may be lucky, especially if you are in the midst of real woodland.

Muntjac

Muntjac are also known as Chinese muntjac, or barking deer, or rib-faced deer. Like roe, muntjac are quite likely to enjoy the border plants in your garden, and again like roe, they are animals of young fir plantations or the sort of woodland that offers dense cover. But they are a strikingly different animal to look at being very small, not more than 46 cm in height at the shoulder, and with 7.5 cm antlers which point backwards.

Muntjac come from the forested hills of southern China and Taiwan, but were brought to deer parks in Britain at the turn of the century. From places like the Duke of Bedford's Woburn estate, they inevitably escaped and set up feral populations, though it has only been since 1950 that there has been a marked expansion. The muntjac have increased in numbers and have spread through mixed or deciduous woodland in south east England, and as far north as Staffordshire and as far south west as the Devon/Somerset border, wherever there is plenty of bramble or rhododendron cover.

Either as solitary animals or in very small groups, muntjac browse on bramble and ivy and on seedling trees, though they are not regarded as a serious pest. They will also take such fruits, acorns and sweet chestnuts as come their way. The buck has a hoarse dog-like bark which it utters in a curiously repetitive manner, every four or five seconds for a period which might last as long as three-quarters of an hour. And the naturalist Michael Clark says it is possible to attract them with the kind of high-pitched squeak made by children's toys.

The muntjac is the smallest species of deer in Britain.

Chinese Water Deer

These are rather larger than the muntjac, though they still stand no higher than 50 cm at the shoulder. And like the muntjac they live in Britain as a result of escapes from captivity in deer parks. Their natural home is the reedbeds and riverside grassland of the Yangtze valley in northeast China and Korea. Over the last forty years they have become established on a fairly local basis in the Whipsnade and Woburn areas.

Water deer are remarkable in that they have no antlers (only the musk deer, also of Asia, shares this character). To make up for this lack, the bucks have long upper canine teeth which provide them with tusks shaped like scimitars. They inhabit less watery grassland and woodland than their Asian relatives enjoy, but when they have the chance they also live in English marshes and reedbeds, the nearest we can offer to a Chinese swamp. Active at dawn and dusk, but rather solitary, they eat grass, vegetables and rootcrops.

Chinese water deer have escaped from zoos and deer parks to breed successfully in the wild.

Reindeer

It is likely that reindeer became extinct in Scotland at the onset of the last Ice Age, although it has been claimed, without much evidence, that the nobility hunted them in remote Caithness in the twelfth century. The reindeer was probably the first ungulate to be domesticated and with the help of this versatile animal man was able to colonise the Arctic tundra. As well as transport, reindeer provided meat and milk, clothing and bedding. In Lapland for example, reindeer oxen have been used for centuries as draught animals to haul freight sledges. The ability to thrive in inhospitable northern latitudes is fuelled by 'reindeer moss', a lichen which grows vigorously in a landscape where precious little else will grow. And their feet are widely splayed so that they can traverse the snow.

In Britain, the reindeer is probably best known as the animal which hauls Father Christmas' sledge across the rooftops, but in reality there is a flourishing herd up in the rooftops of the Cairngorms. The deer were re-introduced to the Scottish Highlands in 1952. Mr Mikel Utsi brought a nucleus from Lapland, and as a result of a great deal of hard work his herd has become a viable entity. The reindeer are culled in a way which maintains the vigour of the stock, providing good meat and hides, and of course they are a considerable tourist attraction for visitors to Aviemore.

They are coloured in a range from creamy white to dark brown, but their most remarkable feature, unique among deer, is that both sexes exhibit antlers, though those of the cows are somewhat smaller. The antlers come in a variety of shapes and sizes. They are shed at Christmas, after the September/October rut, growing again in spring.

Reindeer manage well in the Highlands, eating their customary lichens and also taking plants which are unattractive to sheep and red deer, so they do not come into open competition with these animals.

Reindeer have widely splayed hooves to enable them to travel on snow.

7
DOMESTICATED MAMMALS

Domestication of wild animals has a long history, going back to the Ice Age. The dog was probably the first animal to join us in hunting expeditions, the start of a gradual development, by selection, into some of the astonishing breeds we see at Crufts today. But the dog was followed in due course, through the Mesolithic and Neolithic ages, by other animals which served to provide food, clothing, transport and pest control.

There were certain criteria which had to be met before an animal could be considered a candidate for domestication (though it is highly unlikely that a committee of hunter-gatherers sat round a tree discussing them!) The species needed to be undemanding in terms of food. And they needed to be sociable – pack or herd animals which lived in a society dominated by the principle of a 'pecking order' in which tough and aggressive individuals enjoyed the top of the heap while more placid and submissive individuals 'knew their place' lower down. If animals entertain social relations with each other, then they are more likely to do it with another species, such as man. As solitary animals, cats, for example, don't fit into this category. They tolerate people as co-habitees in their territory, enjoy the food we offer and pay their way by controlling rodents.

From man's point of view, domestication brought the great advantage of higher food production for less effort. From the animal's point of view there are advantages and disadvantages. They receive protection from their enemies and are provided with food and shelter. On the other hand, they step onto a treadmill which requires them to maximise their production of young and their weight in meat and they are subjected to our decisions on the selection process. With control over breeding, Man can change the animal at least to the extent of its genetic potential. If we want lean pigs, then fat pigs won't be allowed in the party. The long-term result has been that domestic stock are less healthy with a greater incidence of disease.

Dog

Ten thousand years ago we were hunters and gatherers of food. As the Ice Age retreated and the new warmth made way for forests, Man chased animals on foot, threw stones at them and then developed the bow and arrow. In Europe and the Middle East, there were pack animals like wolves and jackals hunting in competition with him. Doubtless the wolves carried off some children. Certainly they scavenged remains from the site of the kill and from the camp fire. Jackals, less aggressive and less feared, also scavenged in the vicinity of men. Inevitably some of these animals were taken in to the human community, either as sick or injured specimens which responded to the human urge to offer food and make friends, or as juveniles which had lost parents or been abandoned. Jackals are easy to tame, wolves less so, and doubtless many of those which spent time in the camps would have moved on to rejoin their own kind. But others would have accepted a place

'Wild' goat in Cornwall.

in the human hierarchy and have proved their worth as hunting companions. So the dog would have been regarded as a working colleague, though also possibly a comforting friend.

Through the years dogs have been developed to do a great deal more than hunt for and with us, though there are still plenty of hounds and terriers who do just that. Breeds have been designed as herders of sheep and guiders of blind people, to say nothing of circus performers and lapdogs. 'Piper' dogs give yeoman service even today on the duck decoys which still survive. Bred to resemble a fox as closely as possible, they attract wild ducks into dead-end nets by showing themselves round a cunningly designed series of reed screens.

Working dogs do not always look particularly beautiful. In the show ring they will always take second place to an animal which has a winning expression and holds itself well. But working dogs are selected for efficiency in operation. They tend often to be the result of cross-breeding and this always encourages vigour and strength. Breeding for fashion is bound to cause trouble. Pedigree dogs tend to be designed to please the eye but the result very often is to encourage deformities which would never endure in a wild population.

Working dogs may not win prizes at dog shows but they are well adapted for their tasks. Sheep farmers on steep and remote hillsides would be unable to operate effectively without the help of sheep dogs.

Opposite: we can only speculate on the way in which wolves and jackals became domesticated. As scavengers they would have enjoyed campfire titbits and perhaps sick or injured individuals were absorbed into the human community to become hunting partners and companions.

Goats

In the course of the evolution which developed man from hunter-gatherer to farmer, there will have been a stage during his nomadic life when he exploited animals with a similar wandering disposition which could be moved along from camp area to camp area with him. And some time after the dog was adopted into our life-style the goat was co-opted. Wild goats originate from Europe and Asia and were certainly available to the Middle Eastern nomads who pioneered the processes of domestication. They were well adapted to survive in poor conditions, needed relatively little care, yet produced meat and milk. Their fleece provided a strong fibre which was suitable for hard-wearing clothing and tent material. In fact, a useful all-round animal.

Goats were introduced to Britain some 4,000 years ago by immigrants from the continent. Their natural habitat is impoverished marginal land; they browse in high mountains and indeed we still have herds in the Snowdon region of Wales, as well as in the Cheviots and on some islands. But these animals are not truly wild, they are undoubtedly descended from the domesticated stock which has existed continuously in Britain since these early introductions. Goats have never been highly regarded by farmers. Although their fat has been useful in candle-making and their hair for wigs, the milk and the rank meat has never been specially prized. Often they have been kept simply because they will occupy the rocky and remote parts of a farm and thus deny these areas to the clumsier sheep which would otherwise be in danger of falling and hurting themselves.

Early mariners released goats on remote islands, knowing that they would thrive to provide warmth and sustenance to shipwreck victims. Lighthouse keepers kept them on their remote islands knowing that they would offer a dependable supply of meat and milk if the relief vessel was held up by bad weather. On Lundy, in the Bristol Channel, there was a large herd of

deal of posturing, pushing and shoving. Aggression and submission are the order of the day as the social order is re-established. In open fighting the top billy emerges from a series of horn-clashing charges that may go on for hours. The groups may stay together for the hard winter months, but by February the families have dispersed, and the new kids are born. The young ones will remain in their rocky den for a couple of weeks till they are strong enough to follow the nanny.

In the summer months they may graze alongside sheep, but they will always tend to enjoy the more rocky pastures. Doubtless our present-day feral herds are the descendants of domestic goats which wandered from the rich valley pastures in summer to browse in rocky country from which it was difficult for farmers to retrieve them. In any case, they lost importance as sheep began to replace cattle as the main upland grazer. Nowadays, feral goats exist by courtesy of tolerant landowners, for they are not the forester's friend.

white goats till the late nineteenth century, and they were re-introduced in 1926 by lighthouse keepers who wanted their milk. These soon became feral and increased till they had to be culled, and today there is still a viable herd.

In North Wales there may be several hundred 'wild' goats but the numbers are carefully managed to reduce the possibility of spreading the foot-and-mouth disease which has broken out in the past. Most of the year they stay put in their high rocky fastnesses, coming down to lower slopes in bad weather, for they are shy creatures.

Shy they may be, but they have a world-wide reputation for randiness. They are known as lascivious creatures, so randy that their eyes are permanently narrowed into slits. It is true that they are fecund and have a high reproduction rate, but this is an adaptation to life in inhospitable regions. They suffer a heavy loss of newborn kids so must produce generously when conditions are favourable.

The rut is in September/October, when the normally small and dispersed groups join together in herds of up to several dozen. There is a great

Sheep

Sheep are very close to goats, in terms of scientific classification. Some physical differences are that in goats, both sexes have horns which grow upwards and backwards, whereas among sheep it is only the ram which has horns and they grow to the sides of the head. Goats have a convex forehead, sheep concave. Billy goats have beards and a powerful smell.

Our present-day sheep are derived from the Asiatic mouflon *Ovis orientalis*, and while the root stock are coloured, most modern breeds have been selected for whiteness, since colour inhibits the dyeing of the fleeces. And while wild sheep have seasonal moults, domestic breeds have more or less lost this inconvenient tendency. Farmers prefer to do the job for them by shearing.

The most primitive breed of domestic sheep surviving in Europe is the Soay. Because the herds have existed in isolated island conditions they have survived through the centuries undisturbed by genetic change. Their name comes for the Norse (Soay – Island of Sheep) and they may even be of Norse origin, but certainly they are 'living fossils', relics of the sheep domesticated by Neolithic farmers thousands of years ago.

Soays are small, goat-like animals with bitter-chocolate coats. They are anything but sheep-like in their herding behaviour for they are almost impossible to manage with dogs. When they are disturbed they run in all directions to find a retreat on cliff ledges. There is a small flock at Balmoral and many zoos and wildlife parks have them, but they are best seen on their remote island homes, places like Lundy, Skokholm, Cardigan Island, Ailsa Craig and, above all, St Kilda. On Boreray, one of the St Kilda's group, there is a flock of black-faced sheep which has gone feral to join the Soays.

On island groups like Shetland and Orkney, and around the Scottish coast and the Hebrides, you may see domestic sheep working the tidal foreshore to eat seaweed, showing that they are perfectly capable of enduring hard winter conditions if they must.

Soay sheep on the remote Scottish island of St Kilda.

Cattle

The Stone Age farmer found that he was able to produce enough food to settle permanently. But he would have had to contend with other animals which would also regard his farm as part of their home range. His crops would be raided by cattle and pigs. The solution was to draw them into the spider's web of his protection in return for dues in the form of meat, milk and hides. To this day, the ungulates provide most of our so-called farmyard animals.

The original wild ox, ancestor of our domestic cattle, survived till the seventeenth century in Poland but is now totally extinct. An animal of Europe and Western Asia, it may have lived in Britain till the Bronze Age, but its closest descendants are now the Chillingham herd of 'wild' white cattle which have remained almost as unchanged pure-bred animals, jealously guarded in enclosures for 800 years. Animals descended from this ancient stock may be seen at Chillingham (near Berwick-on-Tweed) where

visitors are welcome in the summer months. Other herds are kept at Cadzow (Lanarkshire), Vaynol (Carnaevonshire), Dynevor (Carmarthen) and the Duke of Bedford's Woburn estate in Bedfordshire.

Thomas Bewick's famous engraving of a Chillingham bull.

The Chillingham herd represents the nearest we can see to the original wild ox, ancestor of our domestic cattle.

Pigs

The wild boar must have been a considerable pest to early farmers, with its habit of ploughing for roots. In much the same way as our garden robin will follow the spade, those wild pigs would have followed farming activities with close interest. In Britain, the wild boar survived in deciduous woodland only until the seventeenth century, but it is still to be seen, and is as vigorously hunted as ever, on the Continent.

Even in the wild the pig exhibits those useful qualities of fecundity, producing anything up to a dozen fat piglets, which have so endeared them to farmers through the ages. But no doubt the Stone Age men would be somewhat perplexed as well as impressed by the sight of a modern pig-rearing house with its serried ranks of factory sows.

The wild boar is still a relatively common beast on the continent of Europe.

Horses

Most of our farm animals have been domesticated for so long that their ancestry is something of a puzzle. The horse is actually a relatively recent addition, an animal recruited not for its meat but because its speed and strong shoulders made it valuable in the field of transport, but even so, the intricacies of its ancestry are the subject of much debate. There are still a few zoo specimens of the Mongolian Prezewalski's horse, one of its more recent ancestors, in existence. Originally there were several sub-species of these horses across Europe, based on the Arab horse and the Northern horse which existed in two forms, heavy and light. And while a shire horse, at 17 hands high, could only be sustained on rich and productive land, in the far north of Iceland the typical pony was small and fuel conscious, providing a measure of carrying capacity but not eating too much.

Like sheep, the Shetland pony, a triumph of selective breeding that stands no more than 107 cm off the ground, can sustain itself on seashore weeds if it has to, yet it is a useful draught animal. On the Hebridean islands there are ponies which have been developed for saddle and pack work which includes carrying in deer carcasses from the hills during the stalking season. Originally bred from Arab stallions crossed with West Highland mares, they have been carefully kept free of the size-producing potential breeding with Clydesdale or other heavy horse would involve. These animals fend largely for themselves, though the foals, yearlings and mares-in-foal will expect some extra feed. On Exmoor, hardy ponies carry Devon farmers when hunting the red deer.

Until the mid-sixties there were ponies which made their living by carrying panniers full of seaweed from the beach and up the precipitous cliff pathways to the potato fields of Branscombe, in South Devon. Sadly, there is no requirement for them any more, as the potato fields are now being planted with caravans for the tourists.

The ponies associated with Dartmoor and the New Forest are commonly described as 'wild', but they are wild only in the sense that they move and breed freely about a fairly large expanse of unenclosed moorland or woodland. They are all marked and belong to well-defined owners. They are hardy, and until the mid-nineteenth century

Horses have been selectively bred for a variety of jobs, from ponies which can just carry a child to shires like these which can haul a heavy brewer's dray.

they were used as pack animals or colliery workers. The introduction of Arab blood has made them somewhat less heavily built and more attractive as riding animals.

There may be something like 2,000 breeding mares in the New Forest population, which is composed of a number of family units, sometimes loosely gathered together in the classic 'dominance hierarchy' of relationships. The number of stallions is controlled at a level of around 120, a figure which is arrived at by careful

judgement of the health and success of the whole population.

In winter the stallions tolerate each other and the colts without much strain, though they tend to stay apart and stick with particular groups of mares. The herds graze open pasture, woodland clearings and lawns by day, even taking gorse and holly in winter, then withdraw to the shelter of the woods at night. Most of the groupings forage within a home range of around 780 hectares. The stallions become less tolerant and more possessive in spring. Foals are mostly born about the

beginning of May and mating takes place a week or so later. And while the young colts soon drift off to join the wider group the fillies stay with their mothers till they are sexually mature, in their second or third year.

Every autumn, on Dartmoor and in the New Forest, the ponies are rounded up in what is called the annual 'drift' for branding or for the market. Most of the colts and some of the fillies go on to the annual pony sales at places such as Tavistock, Okehampton and Bampton in Devon and markets in Central Wales.

Not so long ago ponies were used to haul coal waggons in the Welsh pits.

Cats

Unlike the other domesticated creatures, the cat is a solitary, rather than a social, animal. It serves us as a controller of pests and as a comforting companion. And one of the reasons that our cats today are so little changed by selective breeding is that they tend to make their own decisions when they choose a mate, and so are spared the worst excesses of fashion-breeding.

Cats are highly efficient rodent operatives but when food is abundant they may prefer just to play with their victims.

Our domestic moggies are not descended from the European wild cat but from the North African sub-species, a rather more elegant form with shorter fur, more open face and longer ears and tail than the northern version. They were introduced to Britain before the Middle Ages as vermin controllers and for the pleasure of their company. Of these some chose to enjoy human attachment, some chose to go feral; and doubtless from the very beginning, as now, some were thrown out of the door. Wherever they found themselves, in pampered surroundings, in town squares, farm buildings or wild woodland, cats flourished and continue to flourish. In the wild they soon revert to their natural tabby, they grow larger and their litters increase. Carnivorous by nature they will take kitchen scraps, rats, mice, rabbits and birds, and, if they get the chance they will freely interbreed with the wild cat.

They may seem placid and cuddly enough on your lap in front of a warm fire, but cats are deadly predators by trade. All-round athletes, they can run, jump, climb and swim with ease, and their muscular hind legs power the precision pounce. Small wonder that we regard them with a mixture of warmth and awe. Our relationship with cats is a practical and satisfactory one. Yet when we hear our own dear puss yowling blood-curdling shrieks into the dark night in a frenzy of passion, we are reminded of darker times, of witchcraft and superstition that as civilised people we are supposed to have put behind us. Perhaps, as part of their courtship message, they are telling us that while symbiotic relationships are fine, vigorous domestication is a slippery slope which leads to intensive piggeries, battery hens and other horrors.

Species List

This list gives the scientific and common English names of all the mammal species found in the wild in Britain (excluding whales and seals). (See page 9 for a brief explanation of scientific classification.)

Order Marsupialia (marsupials)
Family Macropodidae — kangaroos etc.
Macropus rufogriscus — red-necked wallaby

Order Insectivora (insectivores)
Family Erinacedae
Erinaceus europaeus — hedgehog
Family Talpidae
Talpa europaea — mole
Family Soricidae — shrews
Sorex araneus — common shrew
Sorex minutus — pygmy shrew
Neomys fodiens — water shrew
Crocidura russula — greater white-toothed shrew
Crocidura suaveolens — lesser white-toothed shrew

Order Chiroptera (bats)
Family Rhinolophidae — horseshoe bats
Rhinolophus ferrumequinum — greater horseshoe bat
Rhinolophus hipposideros — lesser horseshoe bat
Family Vespertilionidae
Myotis mystacinus — whiskered bat
Myotis brandti — Brandt's bat
Myotis nuttereri — Natterer's bat
Myotis bechsteini — Bechstein's bat
[Myotis dasycneme — pond bat] (5)
Myotis myotis — mouse-eared bat
Myotis daubentoni — Daubenton's bat
[Myotis emarginatus — notch-eared bat] (5)
Vespertilio murinus — parti-coloured bat (3)
Eptesicus serotinus — scrotine
Nyctalus leisleri — Leisler's bat
Nyctalus noctula — noctule
Pipistrellus pipistrellus — pipistrelle
Pipistrellus nathusii — Nathusius' pipistrelle ?(3)
Barbastella barbastellus — barbastelle
Plecotus auritus — common long-eared bat
Plecotus austriacus — grey long-eared bat

Order Lagomorpha (lagomorphs)
Family Leporidae — rabbits and hares
Oryctolagus cuniculus — rabbit (1)
Lepus capensis — brown hare
Lepus timidus — mountain hare

Order Rodentia (rodents)
Family Sciuridae — squirrels
Sciurus vulgaris — red squirrel
Sciurus carolinensis — grey squirrel (1)
Family Cricetidae
Subfamily Microtinae
Clethrionomys glareolus — bank vole
Microtus agrestis — field vole
Microtus arvalis — Orkney/Guernsey voles ?(1)
Arvicola terrestris — water vole
Family Muridae — rats and mice
Apodemus sylvaticus — wood mouse
Apodemus flavicollis — yellow-necked mouse
Micromys minutus — harvest mouse
Mus musculus — house mouse (1)
Rattus rattus — ship rat (1)
Rattus norvegicus — common rat (1)
Family Gliridae — dormice
Glis glis — fat dormouse (1)
Muscardinus avellanarius — common dormouse
Family Capromyidae
Myocastor coypus — coypu (1)

Order Carnivora (carnivores)
Family Canidae — dogs
Vulpes vulpes — fox
Family Mustelidae
Martes martes — pine marten
Mustela erminea — stoat
Mustela nivalis — weasel
Mustela putorius — polecat
Mustela furo — ferret (2)
Mustela vison — mink (1)
Meles meles — badger
Lutra lutra — otter
Family Felidae — cats
Felis silvestris — wild cat

Order Perissodactyla (odd-toed ungulates)

Family Equudae   horses

Equus   horse (4)

Order Artiodactyla (even-toed ungulates)

Family Cervidae   deer

Cervus elaphus	red deer
Cervus nippon	sika deer (1)
Dama dama	fallow deer (1)
Capreolus capreolus	roe deer
Muntiacus reevesi	muntjac (1)
Hydropotes inermis	water deer (1)
Rangifer tarandus	reindeer (4)

Family Bovidae

Capra (domestic)	feral goat (2)
Ovis (domestic)	feral sheep (2)

(1) Introduced
(2) Feral
(3) Vagrant
(4) Domestic
(5) Not yet recorded in the British Isles but likely

Extracted from *The Handbook of British Mammals*, G. B. Corbet and H. N. Southern, Eds; Blackwell, 1977.

Picture Credits

Mammal language

Species	Collective	Male	Female	Juvenile	Home
Hedgehog		*Boar*	*Sow*		*Nest*
Mole	*Labour*	*Buck*			*Fortress*
Shrew					*Burrow*
Bat	*Colony*				*Roost*
Rabbit		*Buck*	*Doe*		*Warren* *Stop (nursery)*
Hare		*Buck or Jack*	*Doe or Jill*	*Leveret*	*Form (milking form for young)* *Scrape*
Red squirrel					*Drey*
Grey squirrel					*Drey*
Vole		*Buck*	*Doe*	*Pup*	*Nest*
Mouse					*Nest*
Rat	*Pack*	*Buck*	*Doe*		*Nest*
Dormouse					*Nest*
Coypu					*Burrow*
Fox	*Skulk*	*Dog*	*Vixen*	*Cub*	*Earth (below)* *Burrow (below)* *Kennel (above)*

Species	Collective	Male	Female	Juvenile	Home
Pine marten		*Dog*	*Bitch*	*Kit*	*Den*
Stoat	*Pack*	*Dog*	*Bitch*	*Kit*	*Den*
Weasel	*Pack*	*Dog*	*Bitch*		*Den*
Polecat		*Hob*	*Jill*	*Kitten*	
(Ferret)		*Hob*	*Jill*	*Kit*	*Court*
Mink				*Kit*	
Badger	*Colony*	*Boar*	*Sow*	*Cub*	*Sett*
Otter	*Bevy*	*Dog*	*Bitch*	*Cub*	*Holt (below)* *Hover (above)* *Couch (above)*
Wild cat	*Clowder*	*Tom*	*Queen*	*Kitten*	*Den*
Horse	*Herd*	*Stallion*	*Mare*	*Colt/filly/foal*	
Red deer	*Herd, Mob, Bunch*	*Stag*	*Hind*	*Calf*	*Lair* *Harbour*
Sika	*Herd*	*Stag*	*Hind*	*Calf*	
Fallow	*Herd*	*Buck*	*Doe*	*Fawn*	
Roe	*Herd, Bevy*	*Buck*	*Doe*	*Kid*	
Muntjac		*Buck*	*Doe*	*Fawn*	
Water deer	*Herd*	*Buck*	*Doe*	*Fawn*	
Reindeer	*Herd*	*Bull*	*Cow*	*Calf*	
Feral goat	*Tribe, Trip, Herd*	*Billy*	*Nanny*	*Kid*	
Feral sheep	*Flock*	*Ram*	*Ewe*	*Lamb*	

Tools of the trade

1 Suppliers of . . .

The following suppliers will provide equipment via mail order (write to them for their catalogues). There may be others in your area from whom you can obtain what you need direct.

Clothes
J. Barbour & Sons Ltd, Simonside, South Shields, Tyne & Wear NE34 9PD. First class all-weather drab-coloured outdoor clothing.

Beaver of Bolton Ltd, Gilnow Mill, Spa Road, Bolton, Lancs BL1 4LF.

Binoculars
Carl Zeiss Ltd, PO Box 78, Woodfield Road, Welwyn Garden City, Herts AL7 1LU. Highest quality optics. Remember that for working in poor light at dusk and dawn you need high light-gathering performance rather than extra magnification. 8×30 B/GA for general use, but try the 7×42 B/GAT and the 8×56 B/GAT. (The 10×40 B/GAT is for birdwatchers!)

E. Leitz (Instruments) Ltd, 48 Park Street, Luton, Beds LU1 3HP.

Pyser Ltd, Fircroft Way, Edenbridge, Kent TN8 6HA. Swift binoculars.

Royal Society for the Protection of Birds, The Lodge, Sandy, Beds SG19 2DL. 'Avocet' glasses are not of the highest quality, but they represent excellent value.

Kings, PO Box 17, Dorking, Surrey RH4 2PO. Lamping outfits using quartz halogen bulbs for binocular work at night.

Decoy calls, netting etc
C.T.F. Field Sports Ltd, 11 Langley Park Road, Sutton, Surrey. Traps, nets, rabbit, hare, and fox calls etc.

Theo Fossell, East Link, Lane House, Penn, Bucks. Deer calls.

Patrick Pinker (Game Farms) Ltd, Latteridge, Iron Acton, Bristol BS17 1TY. Fox, squirrel, mouse calls, camouflage netting.

West Dorset Nets, Magdalen Lane, Bridgport, Dorset. Camouflage netting.

2 Societies

British Deer Society, Church Farm, Lower Basildon, Reading, Berks RG8 9NH.

British Hedgehog Preservation Society, Knowbury House, Knowbury, Ludlow, Shropshire SY8 3JT.

British Naturalists' Association, 48 Russell Way, Higham Ferrers, Northants NN9 8EJ.

Fauna & Flora Preservation Society, c/o The Zoological Society of London, Regents Park, London NW1

Ferret Society, Ormsby, Kingsway Avenue, Woking, Surrey GU21 1NX. (Now defunct, but Graham Wellstead still offers advice.)

Institute of Terrestrial Ecology, Monks Wood Experimental Station, Abbots Ripton, Huntingdon, Cambridgeshire PE17 2LS.

The Mammal Society, Harvest House, 62 London Road, Reading, Berks RG1 5AS.

Royal Society for Nature Conservation, The Green, Nettleham, Lincoln, Lincs LN2 2NR (for details of county trusts).

Vincent Wildlife Trust (Otter haven project), 21 Bury Street, London EC3A 5AU.

World Wildlife Fund, Panda House, 11–13 Oxford Road, Godalming, Surrey GU7 1QU.

3 **Nature Photographers' Code of Practice**
Leaflet available from the RSPB, The Lodge,
Sandy, Beds SG19 2DL.

4 **Hedgehog Nesting Box** (page 17)
Write to the Henry Doubleday Research Assoc.,
Ryton on Dunsmore, Coventry CV8 3LG

5 **To record your observations . . .**
Submit your observations to your local natural
history society, or alternatively to the Mammal
Society, who will pass them on for collation to
the Biological Records Centre, Monks Wood,
Abbots Ripton, Huntingdon, Cambridgeshire
PE17 2LS.

Further reading

Some of the titles suggested below are unfortunately out of print (op.). You should, however, be able to obtain them through your local public library.

An identification guide is essential, for instance . . .
BRINK, F. H. van den *A field guide to the mammals of Britain and Europe* Collins, latest edition 1977. Highly recommended.

Then you will need a handbook which gives basic information about distribution, habitat, breeding and so on. Marion Nixon and Derek Whiteley's *The Oxford book of vertebrates* published by OUP in 1972 covers far more than the mammals and is a most useful and well organised book.

The mammal-watcher's 'bible' is *The handbook of British Mammals* edited by G. B. Corbet and H. N. Southern, published by Blackwell Scientific, 1977.

For general accounts of the British mammals the most comprehensive, and also, in my view, the most readable, are:
MATTHEWS, L. H. *British mammals* (New Naturalist) Collins, n.e. 1968.
MATTHEWS, L. H. *Mammals in the British Isles* (New Naturalist) Collins, 1982.

And for a general introduction to world mammals . . .

MATTHEWS, L. H. *The life of mammals* 2 vols Weidenfeld and Nicolson, 1969; n.e. paperback 1974.

For a highly enjoyable personal account of mammal-watching exploits . . .
CLARK, M. *Mammal watching* Severn House, 1981.

For a detective handbook which will help to identify tracks and signs, fewmets and spraints . . .
LEUTSCHER, A. *Tracks and signs of British animals* Cleaver-Hume Press, 1960.
BANG, P. and DAHLSTROM, P. *Guide to animal tracks and signs* Collins, 1974.
BOUCHNER, M. *Fieldguide in colour to animal tracks and traces* Octopus, 1982.

For a fascinating guide to those creatures which have been introduced to Britain, and have become naturalised . . .
LEVER, C. *The naturalised animals of the British Isles* Hutchinson, 1977. op.

For accounts of the history of domestication . . .
ZEUNER, F. E. *A history of domesticated animals* Hutchinson, 1963. op.
UCKO, P. J. and DIMBLEBY, G. W. eds *The domestication and exploitation of plants and animals* Duckworth, 1969. op.
CLUTTON-BROCK, J. *Domesticated animals from early times* Heinemann, 1981.

Books which deal in more detail with families or single species . . .

Insectivores
CROWCROFT, P. *The life of the shrew* Max Reinhardt, 1957. op.
BURTON, M. *The hedgehog* Deutsch, 1969. op.
MELLANBY, K. *The moles* (New Naturalist) Collins, 1971. op.
MORRIS, P. *Hedgehogs* Whittet Books, 1983.
The *Mammal Society Series* published by Nelson: moles, shrews, bats, hares, woodmice, foxes, otters, mink, fallow deer.

Bats
YALDEN, D. W. and MORRIS, P. A. *The lives of bats* David and Charles, 1975. op.

Lagomorphs
EVANS, G. E. and THOMSON, D. *The leaping hare* Faber, 1972; paperback 1974.
LOCKLEY, R. M. *The private life of the rabbit* Deutsch, 1964. op.
THOMPSON, H. V. and WORDEN, A. N. *The rabbit* (New Naturalist special vol.) Collins, 1956. op.
SHEAIL, J. *Rabbits and their history* David and Charles, 1971. op.

Rodents
CROWCROFT, P. *Mice all over* Foulis, 1966. op.
HANNEY, P. W. *Rodents: their lives and habits* David and Charles, 1975. op.
HARRIS, S. *The secret life of the harvest mouse* Hamlyn, 1979.

SHORTEN, M. *Squirrels* (New Naturalist) Collins, 1954. op.

Carnivores
BURROWS, R. *Wild fox* David and Charles, 1968. op.
HURRELL, E. *Watch for the otter* Country Life, 1963. op.
NEAL, E. *The Badger* (New Naturalist) Collins, latest edition 1975. op.
NEAL, E. *Badgers* Blandford Press, 1977. op.

Deer
CADMAN, A. *Dawn, dusk and deer* Country Life, 1966. op.
HARRIS, R. A. and DUFF, K. R. *Wild deer in Britain* David and Charles, 1970. op.
PAGE, F. J. TAYLOR *Field guide to British deer* Blackwell, n.e. 1982.
WHITEHEAD, G. K. *The deer of Great Britain and Ireland: an account of their history, status and distribution* Routledge and Kegan Paul, 1964. op.

Goats
WHITEHEAD, G. K. *The wild goats of Great Britain and Ireland* David and Charles, 1972. op.

And finally, for a book which provides an eminently readable account of our changing attitudes to animals . . .
THOMAS, K. *Man and the natural world* Allen Lane, 1983.

Index

(Page numbers in bold type indicate main text entries. Italic page numbers indicate illustrations.)